BRANCH WATER TALES

Memories of a mountain family

Bill Carver

Branch Water Tales.

Memories of a Mountain Family
Copyright by Bill Carver

Produced and printed in the United States.

ISBN # 09671908-0-0

Library of Congress Cataloging # 98-91045

First edition: 1999

Second edition: 2000

9 9 0 0 0 2

Art by: Shirley Rackley

CONTENTS

UNCLE CAN AND THE LAST STILL

"Canton he, ain't nothin but a no-count bootlegger!" Mama said. "You know that blamed good and well, Will Vance."

"He's your brother!" Dad said. "I want'a take little Quill along when I go over to Bone Valley, to visit with him. Woman, you ain't but five-foot-three; when you're riled up about liquor, your temper makes you tall as a stack pole. You know that."

"The law's always after Canton. What if they come while y'all are there? What if they put both of you in jail? A licker still ain't nothing but the Devil's kitchen!"

Of course, Mama didn't hold to alcohol in any fashion; not even in camphor oil to rub on sore joints. Dad kept some liquor down in the barn, buried in a barrel of shelled corn. To keep it cold, he told me. To hide it from Mama, I figure.

Talk like that scared me. Dad wrapped both his hands around the coffee cup and stared at it, without saying another word.

1

Dad farms the steep hillsides of the Rail Cove and works in the timber. It's Mama's place to run the household, along with my sisters. Her joy is in us kids and her garden.

The next morning, I stood a long time, thinking about the trip I might be taking. I put my left foot on top of the right; at least one wouldn't be on the cold floor. It's a known fact that whiskey makers shoot people for no good reason; least that's the talk that goes around down in the flat country. I've never seen Uncle Can, but I'd heard many a story about him. I hope he don't shoot at people for no good reason.

Ker---plunk, ker--plunk, ker- plunk, the coffee pot went faster and faster as it come close to a boil. The fire in the stove started to roar, so I closed the ash hopper. I rubbed the sleep out of my eyes; hadn't slept hardly any last night.

The smell of the fatback frying told me Mama was stirring in the kitchen. I looked for her to set her foot down and not let me go with Dad. She never brought up the trip while she fixed breakfast. I felt a kind of chill in the air that didn't come from outside. Dad ate and shaved in a hurry; didn't say one word about where we were headed. I followed him out the door.

We turned out of the cove at a little past five that morning. Our old truck labored along the switch backs on Cat Claw Ridge, then snaked down into the Conehetta Gorge. The truck ran hot as we wound our way up Winding Stairs Road, and we pulled off under a big beech tree.

While we waited for the truck to cool off, Dad waved his hat toward Rail Cove, thousands of feet below. "Seems like women are put here on earth to worry and fret about things. Your Mama's picked whiskey."

"I've heard Mama call Uncle Can lots of words. What's a blockader? What's a bootlegger?"

"A blockader, generally he makes whiskey. A bootlegger mainly sells what others make. Some people do both."

Road dust and the smoke coming up through the floorboard nearly always made me sick to my stomach. Our old truck had plenty of both. I took sick as we crossed Tin Cup Knob, but got over it once we climbed down into Bone Valley and the road leveled off some. Dad stopped in front of a large two-story house with two thirty-foot chimneys that seemed to reach the sky. Right through the middle ran an open space, like an inside porch. It put me in mind of a tunnel.

"That open area in the middle of the house they call a dogtrot." Dad pointed at the house and turned the truck off. "You'd do all the cooking in the north end of the house. The south end is for sitting. The sleeping, most time, is done in the loft. That's how they built in time past."

"Where's the licker still?"

Dad's face broke into a big grin. "There's folks who've spent a lifetime trying to find it. Mainly the Revenuers."

The rich smell of tenderloin sizzling on a big Roman Eagle cook stove, made my belly growl as Dad knocked on the kitchen door. Through the open door I saw a small man with short-cut gray hair. He had his collar button fastened, like a store-keep, and he was humming a tune while he cooked. Every time he handled a plate or dish, he took it to a big metal tub and washed it off. Water came in through a poplar bark trough and poured into a number 10 washtub. Another bark trough carried it back out.

He waved us inside. "Come in." The little man's voice was soft, almost like a child's.

He wiped both hands on his apron, shook hands with Dad and rubbed his hand through my hair. "You made good time, I'll have supper directly." He asked about Mom. "Is sister fairing well?"

He listened close as Dad talked. "She's making do fine; maybe, putting on a little."

Then Uncle Can asked about all my sisters, giving their names and ages as he went. How he knew so much about our family without ever seeing them puzzled me. He knelt down in front of me and took my hand. "My name is Canton, but I want you to call me Can. Everybody does."

He asked me about myself and listened close as I told him about school, friends, and such. By the time supper was over, I felt as if I'd known him a long time. How Mama couldn't like this small, neat man with such good manners was beyond me.

"I told Smitty you were coming over; he'll be here in a little bit. Had a turn of corn to take to the mill, over on Jucker's Rough."

This seemed to please Dad. He had told me that Smitty was Uncle Can's friend, for as long as he could recall.

A little time later, a barrel chested man in duckback overalls and a floppy felt hat sailed through the door without knocking. A heavy beard with snuff stains covered his chest. He spit into the big rock fireplace twice, then plopped down in a chair and grinned big. "Hit looked like a young snow, there was so much frost on the hem-pine trees this morning. You-uns all right over in the Rail Cove?"

"Fine as frog hair, split in the middle." Dad said.

All three of them sat around the fireplace telling tales. Smitty spat tobacco juice before he spoke up, every time. I was settling down into bed, over against the wall, and heard a funny noise outside.

At first I thought it was the shuck-tick bedding they always rattle bad in the winter. Then I heard it again, much louder this time. Uncle Can must have heard it too, because he stared at the front door. All at once a loud pounding on the door rattled everything in the room. Dad and Smitty froze in their chairs, rocking forward ever so slow.

Wham! Wham! Wham! This time I figured the door would come clean out of the frame.

"I'm coming," Uncle Can said in his low, meek sounding voice.

Soon as he opened the door, I saw the yard was full of men. Most had battery lights shined on the door, and every one of them had a pistol strapped on his waist or a long gun in the crook of his arm. All at once a big man with a crooked pipe hanging from his mouth stepped in the doorway. His black beard covered most of his face and neck, and a big flat-brimmed hat on his head shaded his eyes. He looked like the boogie-man to me in his big black coat. Nobody had to tell me these were lawmen.

Smitty hand rested on the handle of the pig sticker he carried in his front pocket. I looked it over before; must have been a foot long when it was open. Dad's eyed fixed on the rifle gun above the mantle board.

"Gentlemen, what can I do for you?" Uncle Can asked in the polite tone that he used when he talked about my school.

"We got a warrant to search this place for unstamped whiskey." While he talked, four police cars slid into the yard and slung dirt up against the wall. I counted twenty lawmen and some others stayed outside like guards or something.

"May I see your warrant, please?" Uncle Can said. The big man reached in his coat pocket and brought out a piece of paper. He unfolded it and handed it to Uncle Can. Uncle Can took the paper and walked over to the fireplace. He twisted around to decipher the words by the light from the fire. He studied it for several minutes.

I thought about why Mama said she never wrote to Uncle Can: "Canton never had no book-learnin." She was wrong about that, she was wrong about everything about him.

Uncle Can turned back toward the men, folded the paper carefully and handed it back to the big law officer. "You may search, gentlemen."

The big man stuffed the paper into the breast pocket of his coat and turned to the other men. "Go to it, boys!"

The lawmen searched the house for more than an hour. I heard half a dozen, rattle things as they went through the can house and out buildings. I sat on my bed, scared half to death---they even looked under it. I could have told them there was nothing there. I done and looked.

7

Dad, Smitty, and Uncle Can talked in a low voice without moving from their chairs. Dad and Smitty cut their eyes at the lawmen, like they were fixing to start a fight. I heard Smitty say something that ended, "God Damn law dogs need to carry a good ass whooping."

Uncle Can slid his chair right between them and talked low. They unclinched their fists, but their eyes were still wild and Smitty kept his hand on the knife handle.

One young officer found a pint bottle under the windowsill. He held it out at arms length; like it was a torch, and ran up to the big man with a pipe.

"This ain't no licker," the big man sniffed the bottle. "It's camphor oil. They'ed make us the laughing-stock, if we took that in."

He turned to Uncle Can. "I brought Constable Wilson so there would be no mistake on my part. I've found some sheet copper, rivets, and two tons of sugar."

Smitty spat a stream of juice into the fire. "We plan on doing some serious canning. Might make a little jelly or. . . . . ."

"Very well. As you say." Uncle Can broke in, awful obliging.

The big man pointed to the copper and stuff on the porch. "Load this up, boys."

"What do you say, Lem?" Uncle Can asked a man with a badge that said Constable: Polk County.

8

"I told him that wern't enough for a case. They never found one drap of whiskey. Nothing would do him but take the stuff in. There're all really atter you. He'll file charges, sure as hell."

"Do I need to make bond?" Uncle Can said.

"Five hundred dollars. He knows they'll never convict you here in this county. The trial will be held over in Asheville."

Uncle Can paid the bail bond money. We watched the cars leave, their rear ends drug on the rocks, from the weight of Uncle Can's sugar and stuff.

"Get me a drink, Can." Smitty laughed so hard he lost his breath. "I need it bad."

Uncle Can left the room and came back five minutes later with a big jug of white liquor. Dad and Smitty drank and talked until the wee hours of the morning. Uncle Can acted like nothing had happened.

"Shoot, ain't that Old Luke Tester the meanest, vilest law dog that's been around here in a time and a time?" Smitty said, as he tore through the kitchen door, next morning.

"He's just trying to make a name for himself around here. He broke up a pop-skull ring over in Jackson County," Uncle Can said. "They claim he an educated man, his wife's a professor at the Teacher's College."

9

"Couldn't be," Smitty said, as he slurped down a cup of coffee. "No woman of letters would put up with him. Only school he ever went near wus where they train bulldogs. No decent women-folks will put up with anybody who nurses that pipe full of home-grown tobaccy. Besides, the smoke is plumb green, and on top of which, he ain't never took that blamed old coat off."

"Sun don't shine on any one man's crops all the time." Uncle Can said.

"How's he caused so much fuss?" Dad said

"Old buzzard's got a turn like a biting sow," Smitty said. "He'll sleep all day in his car, parked along some logging road, then roam the mountains all night, a lookin for a way to cause a ruckus with decent folks."

"We'll see him come trial day," Uncle Can said.

"I'd like to see him in Hell," Smitty said.

"How was it you came to know Can?" Dad said, to Smitty.

"I met Ole Can years ago. He was a totin the mail from here in Bone Valley, over the mountains to Heifer Horn Creek. Can, he made the trip ever day. Thirty miles for thirty cents, that was the pay. While I was totin white licker over the same trail."

"Were you hauling whiskey at the time you met Can?" Dad said.

"Hell, no, I was haulin ass! Spent all night out runnin the revenuers, they wus thick as hops. Jumped out on me at the still, at dark, they did. Chased me from one end of Still House Branch to the t'other. They's gained ground, so close they wuz, I div down off a rock cliff onto a ledge. When they came around the top, they kicked dirt on my britches." Smitty held his big hands a couple feet apart. "They'es that close."

"Didn't catch you, I'll bet," Dad said.

"Hell fire no, never have caught me in the mountains. Seven sight races, I've run with'um. That thar was the closest they ever come to catching me." Smitty slapped his legs with his hands.

"Where was Can?" Dad wanted to know.

"I'm a comin to that. I was a restin up on Shin Bone Ridge. I seed this horse and rider a comin along in the shank of the evening---the rider was pert-near-a fallin out of the saddle. I hailed him down and saw he was a holdin this big yeller rattlesnake in his right hand--had to be five feet long. The rattler had struck him on the thigh." Smitty spit a wad of tobacco into the fire. "I got him down on the ground. He had a death grip on the snake's neck--had to wrench it out of his hand."

"Did you know him back then?" Dad said.

11

"Hell fire no, never laid eyes on him before. He was out of his head, didn't know his name." Smitty paused to load his jaw with tobacco.

"Did you take him to the doctor?" Dad's voice was high.

"Wern't no doctors hereabouts back in them times. I threw him up on that horse and took off a runnin for my place. My wife Nellie doctored him straight through for five days. He blame near died, out of his head the whole time. Even though he was in his twenties, by the forth day the hair on his head had turned stone cold gray."

"What did she use to treat the snake bite?" Dad asked the question that was on the tip of my tongue.

"White licker, camphor, snake root and a bunch of herbs. As I recall, there was one she didn't have. A special breed of sassafras that only grows on the Hooper Bald, over in the Snowbird Mountains."

"What did you do?" Dad said, after a spell.

"Shucks fire, I took off a runnin, I did."

"Best we could tell," Uncle Can said, "he covered over a hundred miles that day. Taking in to account the race with the revenuers."

"As soon as he was able to travel," Smitty said, "I took him back to the post office down in Proctor. Postmaster fired him on the spot for letting the mail pouch out of his sight."

"Didn't he know about the snake bite?" I said, before I thought.

"Hell yes he knowed it. I brung the snake's skin to prove hit. Besides, the lock on the mail pouch hadn't been tampered with. Most of them giver-en-ment people a bastard bunch anyhows."

Uncle Can reached for his hat. "We need to get on up to the still house. There's a run coming off today."

We walked for an hour; Dad and Smitty carried a sack of corn malt each that Smitty had brought with him earlier. I followed along behind Uncle Can. We stayed in a laurel thicket the whole way, twisted and turned, until at last we climbed almost straight up on top of a knoll. I lost all sense of where I was.

"How can there be a still here?' I asked myself "There's no water."

As we topped out, they pulled brush off wooden vats and frame works. Under some hemlock limbs sat four barrels, each covered with a white cloth tied down with a thin strip of hickory bark. Smitty studied them close, before he took the cloth off.

Dad and Uncle Can went off for fifteen minutes or so and came back with a big copper boiler. Soon they had it faced with rock and a fire going.

Just up the hill, water started running in a small ditch. I hadn't noticed it when we crossed the small cove, full of laurel. It had been dry when we got here. Then it came to me that I'd seen Smitty do something in a branch back a ways. It looked like he moved a chunk of wood out of his way; he must have changed the water's flow.

"See them pencil marks?" Uncle Can pointed to some marks on the white cloth, so faint you could hardly make them out. "I make new ones ever time. If the lawmen find the barrels, they have to take the cloth off, to tell when it'll be ready to run off. Or else they might have to watch the still for days. If they take off the cloth, Smitty can tell."

"How can they tell if it's ready, without knowing when is was fixed up?" I said

"By the crust of meal on top. We call it the head. It sinks when the time is right."

In less than an hour the rest of the still was set up. A fire of dry locust soon had the boiler hot. Dad gave me the job of raking the leaves off the bank above the still. The damp ground held the smoke close; I couldn't see it from where I stood. Now, we were making whiskey.

"Climb up that hemlock tree." Uncle Can said. "You can see all the way down to Smitty's house. There's a lone bed sheet hanging from the clothesline. If any strangers come up the valley, his woman'll take the sheet down; we'll shut down the still and go home. So you keep a close eye on that sheet and yell if it's gone."

I had me one powerful fine job! I could see the white speck in the valley way off to the south.

Most of the work was really hard. All the men were wet with sweat. If they stopped working on the boiler pot or the heater box, the flake stand needed tending or else the cap on the boiler leaked. The rye or wheat paste used as a sealer blew loose if the cap had too much pressure. When everything was going just right the "thump, thump, thump of the steam as it bubbled through the thump keg sounded like the slow beat of a far off drum. Any free time, they poured up mash for the next run. It was near dark before the work was all done.

Once the boiler was hid, we covered everything with brush. The place looked like nobody had been here in years. Smitty took toe sacks and made a kind of bags he carried over his shoulders, six gallon jugs on each side. Dad swung a pair across his back and they lit out.

Uncle Can took me over to the barrels full of mash. "See, it's in a straight line between these rivets and that white-oak tree." Uncle Can said, drawing a straight line with a pencil. "That's all we got to remember. If it not like that when we return next week, we'll act like we just happened up on it, ginseng hunting."

"The law might see the marks too."

"They'll think these faint marks are where the cloth was folded or where a limb scraped it." He pitched a hand full of dry oak leaves on top of each barrel.

We got back to the house around nine o'clock. An hour later a big touring car came to the house-- from Atlanta, Uncle Can said. They had a big copper tank sitting in the trunk. Soon as we filled it up with liquor they paid Uncle Can and left in a cloud of dust. They said less than two words to any of us.

Dad and I slept together that night. "Why's the law so dead set on catching Uncle Can?"

"They don't care how much whiskey we make or how many folks drink it," he said. "Only that the taxes get paid."

He'd explained it to me just like I was a grown-up, so I tried to ask my next question the way a grown-up would. "So why don't Uncle Can pay the blame taxes?"

"Some of these mountain men cain't bring themselves to pay twelve dollars in taxes on a gallon of whiskey that only cost them seven cents to make. When you study, it don't make sense a-tall."

"Then why don't Uncle Can just stop? He's getting old."

"Men like Can think it's their God-given right to make whiskey. They also know the big bonded whiskey makers are the ones putting the pressure on the politicians--else there wouldn't be so many law all over the place."

We just lay there for hours, watching the fire die out.

"What will happen to Uncle Can, when they try him over in Asheville?" I asked, when I couldn't hold it no longer.

"May be a long time before it goes to trial. They'll try any trick in the book to convict Can. We'll go find out."

I fell asleep thinking about Uncle Can, and the trip to Asheville. Mama will just have to stop siding with the big bonded whiskey makers against Uncle Can. I might give up playing cars and make myself a liquor still when I get back home. Reckon how she'll take that?

We sat around the table after breakfast the next morning, when a family came to the door. Their clothes were mostly rags, and the little girl's mother had to guide her to the door. I thought maybe the girl was feeble-minded or something.

"Please do come in," Uncle Can said, almost bowing as the woman passed him. The man and two little boys stood against the wall while the woman took the chair Uncle Can offered her. She reached up her arm around the little girl's waist like she was holding a post. The woman had on men's brogans with more holes than leather. Her feet had to be freezing.

"Mr. Can," she said, "our little Molly here's a goin blind--they say it's her sugar. They can doctor her over in Knoxville, but we ain't got money for gas to get thar."

"How long will she need to be over there?" Uncle Can said.

"Four or five days."

"Where you planning to stay while she gets her treatment?"

Her head dropped. We'll make do in the truck. Hit ain't that cold at night."

"Excuse me a minute," Uncle Can said. He walked out into the front yard and around the old rusty truck, then came back in. "You'll be needing some other things. Tires for the front of the truck, money for a place to stay and something to eat. A new dress and shoes for yourself and a dress for the child."

Uncle Can pulled out his wallet and gave the woman all but ten dollars of the money the whiskey haulers had paid him last night. The woman's eyes lit up for the first time since she'd walked in. "We'll try to give it back soon as Tyerell here sells his tobaccy."

I saw then, how young she was.

"Will they be able to pay you back?" Dad asked Uncle Can, after they left.

"When I let them have the money, I look on it as a gift. If they pay me back any part of it, I feel like I'm a winner. If they don't, then I've broke even."

Not even an hour passed till an old man and a boy showed up at the door. The man had a piece of paper held tight in his right hand. They came in the living quarters and spoke to Uncle Can in a voice too low for me to hear.

"They want the loan of some money too?" Dad asked later, while he fixed supper.

"No, they got his oldest boy in jail because he failed to register for the draft--the boy didn't know he was supposed to. The draft board claims his birthday is wrote in the family Bible wrong. The people in town are eager to hurt their family, so I made his bond."

"Why do they want to hurt them?" I said.

Uncle Can grinned. "They been known to make a little whiskey."

I scratched my head half the night trying to figure why Uncle Can gave his money away and helped people that took trade away from him.

The next morning Dad and Smitty went to see if they could track up a rabbit, in the dusting of snow that fell late last night. I helped Uncle Can clean the house.

"Want to show you something," he said soon as we swept off the dogtrot.

He led me out to the can house. It was dug deep into the bank, to keep from freezing the can goods and potatoes, just like ours back in the cove. The door had stood wide open ever since the lawmen searched. I reckon Uncle Can closed it once the weather turned really cold.

Once inside, he shut the door part way. As my eyes got used to the dark, I saw him stare at the potatoes in the bin.

"Wan'ta show you something no other living soul has ever seen." Uncle Can said, in a whisper.

He felt along the rough boards that lined the wall behind the bin and pulled out a knot in one of them. He poked his finger into the hole, like he was feeling for something. Out came the end of a small rubber hose. He took a clean pint bottle from his pocket and in seconds siphoned it full of white liquor.

"Go'na give these to your Dad," he said, after he filled a half-dozen bottles and replaced the hose and knot.

"So . . . that's . . . how you got the whiskey the other night right after the lawmen searched all over the place!"

We both grinned.

.

"Remember," he said, "no one knows about this cept us. Not even Smitty." Uncle Can opened the door. "Let's keep it that way."

"How long you had it fixed up like that?" I had a hard time getting my words right.

"The fifty-gallon copper tank? Let's see, back then, I was twenty-two. Put that tank in neigh on to fifty year ago."

I had lots more questions to ask him. Just like I knew he trusted me, I also knew he did not want any more talk about it.

"Will they send Uncle Can to prison?" I said as we drove toward home.

"The fur may fly. We'll go see."

Back home, Mama didn't want to hear how much I liked Uncle Can. Dad and I talked about him every so often. About every time, he told me that his trial for making whiskey had got put off again. Something over a year passed before we got word that the trial was about to commence in Asheville.

I hoped he still meant for us to go--wondered how he'd get Mama to agree. In the end, he said. "Me and Quill got some business in Asheville."

"I heard too." She spat back.

We spent the night with Uncle Can, then headed to Asheville the next morning, early. A short balding man with a full set of dress clothes, met us on the steps in front of this big marble building. He pumped Uncle Can's hand like it was a well pump.

"That's Uncle Can's lawyer." Dad said. "His name is Brent McQueen. He's known all over the mountains as the man you wanted in your corner if you got in trouble."

"You bring me any of that apple brandy you make?" were the first words he said, to Uncle Can.

"I did." A big grin came over Uncle Can's face. "I want to win this case."

Brent McQueen grinned back and slapped Uncle Can on the arm. "Been drinking that brandy going on forty years. What wakes me up of a morning."

He pulled a newspaper from under his arm and read us a story about how after many years of trying, the law had at last caught a big time mountain whiskey maker. Called Uncle Can's name over and over again, like he was one bad sort. The way it was wrote, it sounded a lot worse than I remembered, like they were about to send him to prison for sure. McQueen must have took a delight or saw something funny in it, by the way he crumbled up the paper and threw it down.

We spent the night at Mr. McQueen's home; the fanciest house I've ever seen in my life. It had cloth rugs on the floor. I seemed the only one the least bit worried about the trial. Mr. McQueen just talked about old times and drank a good part of the gallon of brandy.

Later, in bed I turned facing Dad. "Uncle Can, nor the lawyer man, ain't making no plan to win. If it was up to me, I'd spend my time working on a plan: going over and over everything."

At the same time, I heard Dad making the soft whistling sound he does in his sleep.

The next morning the courtroom was packed. Seems like everybody in nine counties came to see Uncle Can tried. Lawmen milled around, thick as fleas. They came to see an old mountain whiskey man sent to jail, I reckon.

"That's the man that wrote the piece in the paper." McQueen, pointed to a man in his thirties with a woman's cape on and a camera box in his hand. The man's head looked like a gourd with a dirty mop draped over it.

I walked over to where he was talking to some lawmen. "They got the meanest judge they could find. When this trial is over, I just might get me a job with one of them big papers, in Charlotte or even--Atlanta."

"They've worked on this hard, for years." One of the lawmen said.

"Oh, It's a cut and dried case." The paper man said. "They'll send that old whiskey maker to the workhouse for sure. Remember, I already said so, in the paper."

A few minutes later, I tried to tell Dad and Uncle Can what he'd said, but they paid me no mind. They laughed and talked calm as you please.

The trial started at ten. Old Luke Tester, the big lawman, stood up in front of the judge, talking loud and pointed with his big crooked pipe. By this time I was really scared.

There was lots of talk, some of it in strange sounding words, and it looked as if Luke Tester took pleasure in every minute of it. The paper man stood close and wrote in a tablet like he didn't want to miss a word. Uncle Can and Mr. McQueen talked quietly, not seeming to care much about what was going on in the courtroom, until when it was McQueen's turn to talk.

"Your honor, sir!" Mr. McQueen bellowed at the top of his lungs. "Can I see the warrant that was served on my client?"

Luke Tester reached into his coat pocket and brought out the neatly folded paper, just as he had back at Uncle Can's house. Mr. McQueen was by his side in a flash. He took the paper from Luke Tester and pranced around the courtroom; waving it above his head. He made two full circles before he took the paper up to the judge.

They talked low among themselves. The judge laid the paper down, only to pick it up a few seconds later and study it some more. He held it up and pointed it at Luke Tester. "Mr. Tester, is this the warrant?"

"Yes, your honor." Luke Tester fumbled in his coat pocket without bringing anything out. "I've kept it right here, next to my heart."

The judge turned to another lawman.

"So say you, Constable Wilson?"

"Yes, I reckon it's been in his pocket."

"Well, it's a warrant to search this man's house, all right. But hell fire—it's twenty-five years old. Case. . . . Dismissed!"

The paper man's mouth flew open, like he had been slapped in the face, with a board. "That old bastard switched warrants. . . ."

We were back on the street by ten fifteen that morning. Mr. McQueen never hushed--he begged us to stay over another day, but Uncle Can wouldn't hear of it.

"Next time you make a run of brandy, save me a couple gallons." Mr. McQueen shook Uncle Can's hand. "I'll come and get it. You just let me know. Better save a gallon for the judge---I'll need something to smooth his feathers down, after this morning."

Over time Dad and I visited Uncle Can, but if Mama wanted to send him anything, she put the notion in Dad's head without owning up to it. Dad knew what took place; he ever let on.

One Thursday some months later, Dad came home with a newspaper under his arm. It showed Uncle Can's house on the front page, with him and Smitty standing in the dogtrot. The words, in big print, under the picture read: A MOUNTAIN LEGEND.

No sooner had Dad laid it down on the table than I grabbed it to see if the paper man from the trial had wrote it. Another picture on the back page was a man in his fifties, with a small derby hat and graybeard. It said he wrote about Unlce Can.

Dad read the story out loud and we all listened. It told how Uncle Can had helped folks and many other good things about him. Mama's face lit up near the end when Dad read the words about how Uncle Can had quit making whiskey, now that he was older and wiser.

"Me and Quill are going to take this paper to Can." Dad said.

"When?" Mama said. She must have known he meant now, for she gathered up a box of things and two strings of leatherbritches. She didn't have time to put the notion in Dad's head. "Take these to Can."

When we got to Uncle Can's place in Bone Valley, Brent McQueen sat on the porch, by himself. Beside him lay one of the papers. After him and Dad spoke a few words, Mr. McQueen picked up the paper. "I drove over from Asheville this morning to show this to Can."

"Can not around?" Dad said.

"No, he and Smitty went ginseng hunting a few minutes ago." McQueen looked at his pocket watch and stepped off the porch. "I must be on my way back, I have court in the morning."

We got back in the truck and headed for home. When we passed Smitty's house both of us busted out laughing. There on the clothesline hung one lone bed sheet.

BESS and the MAD DOG

"Mad dog! Mad dog!" Maude Hillman was the first to see the dog and sound out a warning.

We all looked at her at once. The cold chills ran up my back. We looked at each other; each face seemed to say, "What'll we do."

"Mad dog!" The hoe handle Maude pointed with trembled in her hand. "Lookie yonder! See that big-big black dog coming up the cove road. Hit's done and gone mad."

We all stood still as fence posts and watched the dog snap at every laurel bush and twig he came near; white foam covered the head and chest like soap suds. We couldn't take our eyes off the thing.

"Mad dog! Mad dog!" Maude said. "That's what I've been a warnin you-uns about!"

"Mama," one of the little girls said, "what if it comes across the bridge?"

"Lord-a-mercy youn'ns!" Maude said, "run put the dogs in the barn and get yoreselfs in the house. That dog yonder done and gone mad."

"Cain't we kill it?" Bess, the oldest girl said.

"We ain't got narry a thing to kill it with," Maude said, "your Paw took the gun to work with him."

Mad dogs--animals with rabies were something we dealt with every summer. It seemed the hotter it got the more there were and this summer had been hot and dry. Folks kept their kids hold-up in the house most of the time; there were sightings and rumors every day. Mama wouldn't let me go in the woods and that bothered me a right smart. If we went to visit or to church after nightfall, Mama carried a big coal oil lantern so she could see what lay ahead.

"Mama," one of the small girls said, "we got to try to warn the folks who live on above here."

It was plain to see, right off, that Maude was beside herself with fear. Her head bobbed around like a turkey's while she counted the girls until she came to the tallest. "Bess, it's up to you, child. You're the oldest."

Bess was twelve and the oldest and she let the others know it. Becky was three years younger and I liked her much better, because we were the same age, I figured. All the Hillman girls had blond hair, which was kind of a curiosity here in the mountains, but Mama talked about how pretty it was. Bess's was curly and lighter than the others; maybe that is what made her get her dander up, if things did not go to suit her.

Not an eye moved off the dog or a sound was made as the dog got even with the bridge crossing the creek to the Hillman's house. Once it stopped and looked toward us until sweat ran down into our eyes. The dog snapped at a tall dead weed swaying slowly in the breeze, and passed the bridge.

"Lordy," Maude said, "hurry child, that dog is headed on up the cove."

"I'm a goin. I'm a goin." Bess said.

"I feel like the slaves in the Bible that put blood on their door post," Maude said, "the death angel passed me by."

"I'm going too." I said, and took off running across the garden after Bess.

My folks had brought me over to stay with Maude Hillman, and her girls, while they went to visit with a sick aunt in Asheville. They'll be back on the train tomorrow night.

We waded the creek at the end of the garden and got in front of the dog. Running as fast as we could, we were soon out of sight of the dog. This made us shaky, we looked back every few seconds, like we knew the it was gaining on us.

Bess hadn't said a word, but I knew she was at least a little scared. We always took our time when we walked barefoot in the road, stepped on flat rocks, so the sharp gravel wouldn't cut our feet; now I saw bright red spots where Bess ran.

By the time we reached the first house I was short-winded. "Who lives here?"

"Old Lady Miller and her man," Bess said. "They just moved here from the city. She's a witch."

I followed Bess across the bridge and right up on the porch. Bess hit the door with her fist so hard it rattled. A long time passed. Bam! Bess hit it again, only harder. I felt for sure the door glass would fly into a hundred pieces.

A little old woman pulled back the curtain just enough to peer out. "What do you want?"

"Mad dog a comin up the cove," Bess said. "Is your man home?"

"No he's not." The curtain dropped back and the house went quiet.

Bess turned on her heels and jumped down off the porch. I followed as fast as my legs would move. We were back across the bridge, before Bess spoke. "They ain't got no dogs or cats and I warned the old hussy."

"Is all the houses across the creek like this one?" I said.

"Not all."

Before we turned back up the creek, I saw the dog round the curve below. He seemed to travel faster, now that no bushes hung over the road for him to bite at. Bess turned up the cove, running like a scared haint. We ran, what must have been a mile or so, before we stopped at the top of a long hill.

"How long is this creek?" I said.

"Nobody rightly knows; some men-folks argue seven miles. Others claim ten. They don't know. No way to get a car or nothing up here to measure it. It ain't nothing but a wagon and sled road."

"It's about as much up and down as it is far and wide." I said.

The big flat boulders on top of the ridge felt good on our feet. We'd been stopped for little or no time when we saw the dog coming up the hill, snapping at everything that moved.

"Damn that thing!" Bess said, and took off in a dead run.

I had never heard a girl cuss before, but I'd never run from a mad dog either.

After a long sprint, we came to a cluster of houses in a clearing. The bridge was plenty wide and we wouldn't have had to slow down if the thing was not about to fall; planks missing everywhere. The yard was full of dirty-faced children, playing among the boulders; some rolled an old car tire, others played tag. We ran up in front of the first house. It did not have a porch or stoop of any kind and the door stood wide open.

"Mad dog!" Bess yelled. "There's a mad dog a coming up the cove!"

A middle-aged woman came to the door. "What's all the commotion?"

"A mad dog's a comin up the cove," Bess said, "right behind us."

The woman rubbed her hand on her dirt-stained apron. A smirk covered her weather-worn face. "Are you sure, girlie?"

"Yes'em."

"Where's it at? I don't see nothin."

"Hell yes, I'm sure!" Bess said, her back straight as a rail. "Mama sent us to warn you-uns. Is Mr. Ross Turner here-a-bouts?"

I looked for the woman to slap Bess; Mama'ed sure pop your jaws if a young-un, sassed her that way. Course, Mama would never bring it on by acting the way the woman did.

"No, he ain't," the woman said.

Bess stood her ground. "You-uns got a gun?"

"Naw," the woman said.

A big boy came to the door. He looked older than Bess by a good four years, and he was at least a foot taller. "Yes we do, but we ain't got narry a shell for hit; ain't had since last fall."

"Well you've been warned," Bess said.

"I ain't a feared of no dog a tall," the boy said. "What's you'uns name?"

The woman turned to the kids that had crowded around. "Get them dogs put up, boys. You little'uns scamper on home and warn your folks. There's a mad dog a comin this way."

Their little eyes got big as saucers. By the time we crossed the bridge and made our way up the road, there was not a soul in sight at any of the houses.

"I thought that big boy would've at least go with us." I said.

I couldn't make out what Bess said, but the last part sounded like, "that old bitch."

A little while later we stopped at a spring box on the side of the road. The cold water splattering on our feet felt good. Bess's curly wet hair looked like a sheep's wool in a winter storm. I figured I looked as bad.

"I don't think you'd care if that woman had to take thirty shots in the stomach." I said.

"You said that right, still, I feel for them little ones back there."

It came to me; they did hold their bellies as the woman talked about the mad dog. What a body don't know is sometimes worse than the threat.

"We'd better go," Bess said. "I'm sure the Codys have a gun."

At the same time we saw the dog trot around a bend, not fifty yards away. We broke into a run.

The Cody place was barely across the creek. A thirty-foot-high porch stuck out almost over the water. At least it had a good bridge, made out of railroad timbers. We didn't slow down any as we ran across. By the time we had climbed the steep steps, we danced and rubbed the creosote and tar off our burning feet.

The house was shut up tight. The only sign of life was a lone gray cat sitting on the porch rail.

"Anybody to home?" Bess called.

". . . . Meow," the cat said, like it was hungry.

Bess shook the front door. "Hello."

"Ain't nobody here. . . ."

A cow bawled at the far end of the house. We both jumped back against the rail. It buckled until we were out over the water. I grabbed a post and held on.

"Grab that cat." Bess said, as soon, as she caught her balance.

I caught the cat and followed her around the house, as the cow bawled again. "What'll I do with this cat?"

"Throw it up in the shed loft," she said. "I'll drive the cow up."

I followed around with the cat held in the crook of my arm. The cow looked at us a bawled again. "What'll I do with this cat?"

"Throw the thing up in loft of the shed, like I said."

The little jersey cow had a half-grown calf with her. The calf played and dodged as Bess drove them toward the shed. I got behind the door; the cow had hooked horns as sharp as knitting needles. The calf bolted past before the cow was half way through the door. The cow backed out and followed it back up in the pasture.

"Damn," I heard Bess say.

I tried to see if the dog was coming, but the house blocked off most of the view. I tried to look at everything; my head bobbled from side to side, like an owl. The dog sure had made me jumpy.

Two more times Bess drove the cow and calf part-way into the stall, just to have them bolt back out again. I tried to help. We pushed the door against the cow's rump but she braced her feet and we couldn't budge her.

"Leave her be," I said, but I knew Bess had too much backbone to quit.

This time Bess put her shoulder against the cow's rump and shoved with all her might; her face got red as barn paint. I joined in and we held our own, but gained only an inch or two.

"Bess, what in blazes are you doi. . . . ."

"I'm tired of foolin with you!" Bess said, from behind me.

I didn't see it coming until the pitchfork hit the cow in the rump, inches above my shoulder. The cow lunged forward, knocked the calf up against the far wall, and kicked me in the belly.

Bess slammed and bolted the door. "Kick now, old sister."

Once we got back up on the porch, the dog was even with the bridge. We caught our breaths as we watched it come on up the road, right below us.

"Are you hurt?" Bess said.

"No."

"Why did we climb back up on this porch?"

I rubbed my belly and wandered but couldn't come up with anything other than. "I think the poor thing is blind."

The dog looked up at the porch, its mouth drooling, fangs showing. My belly began to hurt bad as I thought about the shots, or was it because the cow kicked me?

"We've got to warn the others and put it out of its misery," Bess said.

"Reckon we can kill it with a rock?"

"We'd have to get powerful close. It's a big scutter." The dog slowed down and looked across the creek at the house. It started down toward the water. Bess looked at me.

"It must have seen us," I said, trying not to blink an eye or flinch a muscle. "He's headed for the steps."

I couldn't keep my mind from wandering back to the tale the Reverend Laban told a few weeks back. One night, as he walked to work down at the tannery; Mr. Si Jones had been bit by a fox. The wound healed right up and he thought no more about it. A few days later he had trouble even swallowing water. As he grew sicker, he knew he had rabies. He went to the county jail and asked to be locked up, so he wouldn't bite anybody as he faced death. Living way back up on Lick Log, he had never heard of the shots.

They gave him the shots right away, but it was too late. The preacher told of the terrible death that followed, leaving out nothing. Even the men-folks had tears in their eyes.

"If it starts up the steps," Bess said, "we'll break into the house."

The front door was made from two-inch thick oak boards and a brass lock the size of my fist hung in the hasp. The only window was even with our eyes now, but they were five feet above my head when we stood on the steps. It might be our best bet, but I tried to come up with something else. "Cain't we jump off the other end?"

"Too high," she whispered. "We'd be killed on them boulders down there."

I knew the dog seen or smelled us, because it stared at the porch like it was spellbound. I looked at Bess; she was white as a sheet. More time passed. Neither the dog nor us moved a muscle. I looked back at Bess. She pulled her hair back from her face. I felt the sweat run down the back of my neck. The dog waded into the water. There was nothing bigger than the ivy vines on the porch post to fight with.

All the sudden, the dog stopped and lapped up some water. I sure could use a drink myself; my mouth's so dry, when I spit it's like a ball of cotton.

A few seconds later the dog was back on the far bank. He vomited and coughed, like he was a dying. I hoped the end was near, and felt sorry for the critter at the same time.

"Iff'en he hadn't took that drink," I said, "we'd be in a heap of trouble now." I followed Bess across the porch.

"Shut up and run!" Bess said.

We ran down the steps and around the house. We made our way through the corn patch. In a minute we were in a maze of tangle-foot laurel and saw briars. It was a snaky-looking place, but we didn't have the time to worry about that.

"Damn!" I heard Bess say. "Ain't makin no time through this thicket."

"Maybe the dog died."

"Don't you wish."

As we climbed up over the rocks onto the road, our hands and arms bled. I saw the dog coming, not over rock-throwing distance away. I picked up a rock and threw it as hard as I could. I missed.

"Move your butt!" I heard Bess say from a little ways up the road.

"How far is the next house?" I said.

"A far piece."

"Good." I took off, never wanting to get close to the dog again.

I didn't say anything to Bess, but the dog was tracking us and it moved much faster when we were on this side of the creek. We ran in a fast lope until our breaths gave out.

"Whew. . . ." Bess said, as we came to a bridge leading to a white-framed house. "This house belongs to Franklin and Ada Davis—they're old but they'll help. I just know they will."

Bess's foot slipped through a broken board in the bridge and a nail cut her right leg. When she pulled her leg out, blood ran down over her knee. "Damn!" she pulled her dress up to her waist and looked at the cut.

Bess was one strange girl. I tried not to look, but it didn't seem to bother her in the least, if I did or not.

"Is it cut deep?" I watched the blood run on down her leg.

"See, a right smart." She wiped the gaping cut with her dress-tail, then ripped of a piece and tied it around her leg. "I'll put some red-worm oil on it when we get home."

"Maybe we can get some salve at this house." I said.

She dropped her dress. "Let's get a going."

The house sat well back from the creek, up on a high knoll. Bess did not stop in the yard this time either; I followed her right up to the door.

"Mad dog a comin!" Bess said, to the little gray-haired woman that answered the door.

"Goodness gracious alive, child you look a sight. I'll fetch you some water."

"Don't rightly have time," Bess said. "Do you have a gun?"

"Franklin, O,o,o. oh! Franklin, bring your gun."

A man's voice came from the rear of the house. "What's that you say?"

"Fetch your gun," the woman said, "and shake a leg."

"What's that you say woman?" The voice said from somewhere back in the house. "What you a carryin on so for?"

"Do you have a dog, or a cow, or anything we can put up for you?" Bess said.

"No," the woman said, "just that old mama cat thar on the mantle. Ill fix you something."

A very old man came hobbling through the door. He was barely able to stand. His hair was as white as the woman's; only his hadn't been combed in a while; hers was put up in a granny knot, all neat like.

"Where's your gun?" the old woman said.

"Hit's over the bed yander, like its all'us been."

The woman walked right up in his face. "A mad dog's a comin up the cove. Do you hear?"

"I see, I see." The old man backed through the door.

A short time later he came out with an old army rifle from some war long past. It was blamed near as long as he was tall. Thump--Thump, it hit the floor as he used it for a walking stick. He almost fell over trying to put a shell in the thing. The old woman and Bess steadied him until he got it loaded. I held the door open, as he half-walked, half-fell out onto the porch.

Bess leaned over close to my ear. "I sure hope he shoots better than he walks."

"Who's these folks?" The old man blinked as he talked. "Cain't we fix'em somethin. They look a fright."

"Maybe I can shoot the gun." I said, to Bess.

The woman must have heard, for she looked at us. "Franklin was a top marksman in the war."

"Which one?" Bess said.

"The one across the waters; the big'en."

The dog moved, on up the road, even with the house. The old man wrapped the sling around his arm and leaned over the porch rail.

"Whar's the dog?" he said.

"Thar it comes." The woman pointed toward the road.

"Whar? Yeah, I see it."

Boom! The big old gun fired; knocked the old man all the way across the porch. I saw the dirt fly as the bullet hit the bank way above and off to the side of the dog. The dog paid it no mind and for sure he had not slowed any. He might even be traveling faster.

"Did I hit it?" The old man said.

"Naw," the woman said. "I couldn't rightly tell, but it's a comin on."

He raised the weapon again, trembling so the barrel quivered like a pine limb in a storm.

Boom!

This time I never saw where the bullet landed. I'm not even sure it hit the mountain.

"We must go and warn the others," Bess said.

"Won't you tarry an set a spell," the woman said. "I'll fix you-uns a bite."

"No," Bess said. "I'll come again and we'll visit."

We jumped down off the porch as the big gun fired again. I felt sorry for them; in times past they sure would have been a great help.

As we raced for the creek, I heard him say. "Did I hit the critter?"

"Run as hard as you can." Bess said, It's getting harder and harder to stay ahead of that thing."

There was not much water in the creek this far up and the gorge walls were steeper and higher. Even up the stream bed the going was slow. We slid and fell on the moss-covered rocks. Now we had to climb over big rocks on the bank to get in the road in front of the dog--one more time. As we climbed up a rock cliff, Bess grabbed my arm and jerked me into the road. "Hurry! Hurry! Hurry!"

We were almost on top of the dog; not ten feet away. It lunged at a low hanging grapevine, its foamy mouth snapped. The foul odor of its breath tied my stomach in knots.

We ran and ran and ran, not to get ahead, but from plain being scared. I did look back once. The dog was trailing us, and every time we got back in the road, it gained ground.

"Is all the houses across the creek?" I said.

"The last one ain't."

The next house, if you could call it a house, sat up in a laurel thicket among more big boulders. If it hadn't been for the foot-log across the creek, I'd never guessed there was a home place here.

The house was made out of sawmill slabs standing up right and we could see inside about anywhere we looked. The roof was tar paper, torn loose around the edges. The shed we put the cow in back down the road would have made a much safer home. When Bess hit the door, the whole shack shook. I know I could have knocked it down with a stick of cord-wood in no time. I hoped that there was no one here.

Bess struck the door a little harder. A young girl opened the door. She didn't look a day over fifteen. Her straight black hair fell on small thin shoulders. Two kids held onto her dress tail, neither coming above her knees.

"There's a mad dog on the way up the road," Bess said, barely above a whisper.

The young woman did not say a word. She just started to cry in long sad moans that caused her body to shiver and tremble like a wounded fawn.

I looked around the shack, for a dog, cat, cow, chickens, or anything to put up, but there was nothing. With this little water in the creek, this far up, the dog might not pass us by.

"Are you here alone?" Bess said.

"Yeah, my man's gone off to work in the cotton mills."

Up until now, I'd hoped this girl might be keeping the children for her folks, who were close by and would help. Now I knew this wisp of a girl standing in the doorway, with the babies, was their mother.

"Do you have a gun?" Bess said.

"No," the girl said. "He had to sell it to get money to live on until he got paid."

I looked inside the door. The dirt floor held a wood stove, bed, table and three cane-bottom chairs. There was no loft, not even a ceiling in the place. If it wasn't for the kids, we'd have a better chance running. It sure did not offer much to fall back on-------if the dog crossed the creek.

"We'll stay with you till it passes," Bess told the girl, as I walked by. "The dog ain't crossed the creek yet."

"Animals have a way of knowin iff'en folks are a skeered off'em," the girl said between sobs.

"Well," Bess said, "if the damn thing crosses the creek, we'll fight it; that's all."

We followed the girl into the shack. I found a knothole, eye level that faced down the road. Time passed ever so slow. I searched for some wood; all animals are afraid of fire-but there was not a stick of wood anywhere.

I pointed at the rotten boards in the back of the house. "Is the last house like this one?"

"No," Bess whispered, "it's a good house, but they have lots of dogs, chickens, cows and I think a couple of mules. . . . . As well as a bunch of kids."

"Like you said, the dog hadn't left the road yet."

"Only thing is, that house is right smack in the middle of the hollow and the road ends there."

"How far is it?" I said. "It'll be dark in an hour."

"Quarter mile or less."

I went back to watching the road. I scratched my head until my hair hurt. A home place right smack in the middle of the hollow, lots of livestock, kids, no creek for a barrier, and not far away. For sure, we'll have to pull off some trick. Dad had a saying about a fix like this: "You cain't go right on dodging lighting. Sooner or later you make a mistake."

I came to myself as the black bulk of the dog showed up against the white rocks in the road. Bess saw it too. The dog trotted through the ankle deep water by the foot-log and made a beeline for the shack.

The girl must have seen it too. "Lordy! what'll we do?"

I looked around the shack for something to fight the dog with. An eight-inch butcher knife was all I found.

Bess turned the table on its side and pushed it against the door. The girl was beside herself with fear. She stood still and cried, low mournful sobs.

I picked up the children and held them in my arms. Their frail little bodies seem to be weightless. They did not make a sound, but their eyes told a lot.

We waited for what seemed like forever. My thoughts strayed back to a time about a year ago, when one of our best hunting dogs bit a boy who threw rocks at it. It was just a scrape on his hand, but it had broke the skin. We had lots of hunting dogs, but Dad didn't hold to one biting a body. When Dad saw what had happened, five minutes later he shot the dog, took a broad ax and chopped its head off. I got real mad when he dumped the bloody head in a flour sack and headed for town, like he was going to show it off.

I told Mama what had happened.

"He's gon'na send it to the state to see if the dog has rabies," she said.

Dad, Mama and even I worried until word came back in the mail that the dog didn't have rabies.

Not knowing where the dog was or what it was up to made it all we could bare. I wished the girl would stop all the crying, but there was no way I'd say anything. Not for the world.

I heard the dog sniff at one of the cracks. I turned to see its black form walk along the front wall. The dim light and the sweat pouring down in my eyes made it hard to see. I wished it would growl or make a sound of some kind---at least, we'd know what it might do.

"Bess!" I said, "he's a goin around that corner!"

She grabbed the table and shoved it up against the rotten boards along the back wall. I saw the dog's head poke through a crack a foot from the table. I handed the little ones to the girl and raised the knife. Bess slammed the table hard against the wall; knocked the dog's head back outside.

"Ahee! Ahee! Hee!" The girl screamed.

Then everything went quite in the shack. The only sound was the sharp clap, clap sound of the dog's jaws, when it snapped. I wanted to puke, from the foul odor of the dog's breath or fear.

The sound of the dog snapping stopped. More time passed. Maybe the dog had left. I looked at Bess; she held out her hands with the palms up. I felt like something was slipping up on me. I turned my head so fast, I about fell on my back. There was nothing there. More time passed.

I took the little boy back into my arms. "It'll be all right." I said.

Wham! The dog tried another crack in the wall, with more force.

"Here he comes!" I said.

"You'll not bite nobody in here!" Bess searched for a weapon.

The dog's whole head and neck was inside now. His shoulders forced the rotten boards apart. Its ugly black head swung from side to side. Foam dripped onto the floor.

"Aheeee!" The girl yelled.

Bess slammed the table in front of us; still the dog gained. She broke off one of the table legs and frailed the dog with all her strength. I shoved the little boy into the girl's arms and raised the butcher knife. We pushed against the table with every ounce of our power. The dog's fangs raked the table top as Bess hit it again and again. We smelled its breath all over the shack. I tried to get enough room to use the butcher knife, but Bess was in the way. He gained on us. I reached over the table and brought the knife down as hard as I could. I felt it land, but couldn't see where. It didn't feel like the dog's head, but it had hit something. I sure hope I hadn't Bess's hand.

A sharp pain stung my hand. I slung my arm up. I lost my grip on the knife. The dog had bit me or Bess had hit me with the table leg. Anyway, I had lost my only thing to fight with. She went right on mauling the dog's head, her; face got redder with every lick. We pushed the table until the dog backed out.

Breathing in short pants, Bess said. "Did the knife get him?"

"Don't know; could have missed. Anyhow, I've lost the knife."

"He didn't bite you, did he?"

I rubbed my sore hand; there was no break in the skin. "No, I think you cracked my knuckles with the table leg. You hit hard."

She looked dumbfounded. In the fight she had not known that she hit me. We stood and looked each other in the eye.

I don't know how long it was, thirty minutes most likely, but it felt like thirty hours passed with no sound or sign of the dog. I broke off two table legs and handed one to Bess.

Color settled back into Bess's face and her hand didn't tremble like it did. The girl just made low moans.

"It's almost dark," Bess said. "We've got to know if that dog has left."

"I'll go," I said, glad in a way to be out of the shack. I opened the door a few inches; the dog was nowhere in sight.

I found him a few minutes later, not ten feet from the house. A stream of blood ran down from his neck, and left a bright red puddle in the black dirt.

I ran back around the house, almost yelled. "He's dead!"

Bess had stacked up everything in the shack and the girl and kids were on top of it. She stood with the table legs raised.

I hugged Bess.

"We'll need to clean this mess up," Bess said, as she lifted the kids down like nothing had happened.

I went outside and found an old shovel with half a handle. I covered the blood with dirt and dug a big hole between two rocks.

Once I turned the dog over I saw the knife in its throat. I had come within an inch of missing; but the knife had somehow found its way into the dog's neck.

I drug the dog into the hole, filled it up, and rolled a big black rock on top.

Bess tried every way in the world to get the girl to come with us. "I'll see nothing happens to you."

It was no use; we left as the last rays of light parted the high tops of the Snowbird Mountains.

"She sure cries a lot," I said to Bess.

"She's got a lot to cry about,"

I met Mama and Dad when the six o'clock train came in the next evening. On the way home, I told them about the dog. I left out the part when Bess cussed. When I told them about the girl crying, Mama set her teeth, like she does when she was going to act, come hell or high water. "We've got to go to the store."

"The store's closed." Dad said.

Nothing would do her but help the girl. "We'll open it up."

Dad didn't fuss. He knew she had her mind set. She did not show it like Bess, but in a way she was ever bit as strong. When we reached the store, Mama was out of the truck in a flash. She pounded on the door with all her might. In no time we loaded up four boxes of goods and were on our way.

We bounced over boulders and scraped the banks; somehow Dad was able to drive his truck up to the foot-log. I went along, to show them where the house was and to show Dad where I covered the blood. He wanted to make sure nothing lapped up any of it and went mad.

"You-all wait right here," Mama said. "I'll ask her if it's all right to bring this stuff in."

I never heard Mama say what she and the girl talked about and she never brought it up; not to me anyway. I felt good, going home, knowing they would have plenty to eat now.

Saturday, Mama, Dad, Preacher Laban, and his wife Ruthie rounded up a whole truck load of stuff and went back to the shack.

Mama looked really hurt when they got back. The shack had been empty. We never heard a word from them again. All we ever knew: the girl's name was Basha.

I lost account of Bess for a few years, then one Saturday, in early spring Dad asked if I wanted to help him take the dogs down to the forks of the road. "Get'um vaccinated for rabies ever year."

There were several other people and lots of dogs, like is common here in the mountains.

I knew Bess's hair the minute I saw her. She had put on a few pounds under the white coat she wore, but her turn was the same. She gave shots and orders like she had done on the creek years earlier.

We hugged and talked for a few minutes, then I got back out of the way.

A young man and girl dressed in white kept saying "Yes Ma'am," as Bess spoke to them.

Then the young man whispered to me, "She's the top ranking student ever to enter the veterinarian class at any school in the state. Yet she has us out every week-end, vaccinating dogs."

"I could tell you a tale," I said.

OL' SALLY and the HIGH-DOLLAR HOG

It was Sunday morning when it happened. I sat playing at the end of the barn hallway while Reek, our neighbor, done the feeding. He turned the horses out of their stalls. They milled around as always at the far end of the hallway. I was picking up my wooden cars when I heard a noise.

In place of wandering out into the pasture, like they all ways had, the horses charged down the hallway straight toward me! The hard clay shook under me as their big feet hit the ground. My skin crawled, but I couldn't get the rest of me to move.

"Lay low, Little Bit!" Reek hollered, once he saw what was about to take place.

Reek lives a quarter mile up the road from our house and works with Dad when he not hunting or fishing. He spends a part of every day at our house. Mama says it's because he lives alone. I figure the fact that he's a hardy eater and she is a great cook is why he takes at least one meal with us every day.

I can tell that Reek is somewhat older than Dad but nobody knows just how old he is. He don't know when his birthday is. Fire burned their family

Bible before the war. He gives what every date comes to his mind when someone asks him. Sometimes they are as much as ten years apart. This bothers Mama some from time to time. I figured out, Reek, he don't know and he could care less about the whole matter.

"When and where was Reek born?" I said to Dad while he sharpened the mowing blade one morning.

"There ain't no telling," was the only answer I ever got.

I fell on my face and started to cry. At first I tried to crawl out of the way, but my legs trembled so, seemed like they wouldn't move me. The horses' feet hammered; the ground shook and the noise grew until it sounded like rolling thunder. Clay dirt clods stung my back as the horses kicked it ahead of them, I knew I was going to get hurt.

I covered up my head with my hands and waited; my sides heaved. They looked big as circus elephants coming down the hallway toward me. A big gray mare led the way. About five feet before her feet hit me, she jumped and sailed out into the barnyard. The others jumped when they reached the same spot, like sheep over a fence. I watched out of the corner of my eye. Being so close together they couldn't see me. They only jumped as they came to the place where the gray mare had.

"Shaw, shaw. Boy!" Reek jerked me to my feet seconds after the last horse sailed out into the barnyard. "Glory be, glory be."

I was still crying, not able to catch my breath. Reek brushed the dirt and dust off me. The veins on his bald-head stood out like half grown grape-vines.

He grabbed his hat off the ground and fanned my face. "Shaw; that first horse, what saved you, jumped like she did."

I saw the ease come in Reek's face as I got to my feet. He nor I ever brought up what happened again.

I was just five-past when the giant logging company ran a railroad spur up the main creek. Later Dad and Reek started to work for them. They wouldn't work for a company that cut everything as they came to it. Dad called that slash logging.

"This outfit is different,' Dad said. "They log the old-timey-way. Use stock to skid out the ripe timber and leave the balance to grow."

"Shaw," Reek said. "That thar's a fact."

The teamster boss rented our barn and pasture to keep the company's horses in at night and on weekends. The oxen, they left in the woods.

Every night and morning, Dad and Reek drove big draft horses through the low gap between Rail Cove and the logging job.

"Shaw. Shaw. This mare's feet big as a number five washtub," Reek said, one Saturday morning as he pitched a red-hot horseshoe into the water barrel.

"We better have them bring another load of hay next week," Dad said.

Most of the time, there were cuts, scrapes, bruises, and sprains on the horses, from the rough work the horses done. On weekends, Dad and Reek mended the gears and doctored the stock. Before the men came to supper at night they fed and groomed the horses. Then, every morning, while Mama cooked breakfast, they did it again.

I felt close to the big gray mare--after all, she had saved my life. Well, maybe it was Reek who really done it. I never figured out what caused them to jump over me.

In a few months the loggers had worked their way so far up the river, Dad and Reek barely had time to sleep any. By the time they fed and tended the horses at night, it was time to start the morning work.

One Friday a man came walking down through the potato patch, toward the barn. He was a small man with a black bow tie and a little derby hat. He was clean-shaven, with small blue eyes, little ears and thin lips, what Mama would called "fine features."

"Shaw," Reek said, "timber boss a comin."

"Here comes the little Englishman," Dad said.

"What's an Englishman?" I said.

Neither one answered, as the man walked into the hallway, stepping like if he was walking on hot coals.

"Good evening gentlemen, we're going to have to move our teams farther up the river." The little man twirled his hat in his hand. "We have logged out this section, you understand."

Dad nodded his head. "We moved the skidder again last week. They pushed the railroad half-way up the river."

"Correct," the man said. "The bunk cars are going the fortnight."

"Come Monday," Dad said, "we'll bring the extra harness to work, with us."

"Splendid," the man said. He shuffled his little boots about, like he wanted to dance. "Will you and Reek continue in our employment?"

"Least till crop-making time," Dad said.

"Jolly good."

He placed his hat back on his head in a flash; seemed like every move he made was at the same speed. Spinning on his heels the little man walked through the hallway, stopping long enough to study each horse. He took stock of each set of gears the same way. Picking up a set of brichen and a bridle, he looked at them for just a second, then hung them back on the post real quick, like they were hot.

"Splendid, splendid," he said. "You have kept this harness in a good state of repair."

"Shaw," Reek said. "Not a mark no where's on them horses, not even their withers. Good gears don't mar up stock."

"Moreover." The timber boss talked as fast as he moved. "We need to settle our account today-- for the keep on the horses, you understand."

"I can come by the office later," Dad said.

"On the contrary. I like to pay when due."

"Well, all-right," Dad said.

Reek walked between them. "Shaw, it don't differ."

"Would you consider taking the gray mare as payment?" The man said.

"I lean more toward a good mule when it comes to farming these hillsides," Dad said. "But, let's see how it works out money-wise first."

"She is a fine Belgiam mare, as you know," the man said.

"Shaw, shaw," Reek said. "What it is you want to get rid of her fur?"

"As you are aware, the deeper we go into the Nantahala Mountains, the steeper it becomes," the timber boss said. "We will be skidding down very steep grades, and she simply cannot run fast enough to keep ahead of the logs."

"How much is she worth?" Dad said.

The man fumbled in his vest pocket for a little black book. "First, my records indicate we owe you for seven months, at the agreed price of fifty cents a day."

Reek nodded. "Shaw, that's ke-rect."

"That comes to a total sum of one hundred and five dollars," the timber boss said.

My eyes got big. I had never heard of so much money. Reek took a small stub of a pencil from his breast pocket. He spat a wad of snuff on the end and commenced figuring on the palm of his hand. He wiped it off on is knee before I could see what he wrote.

"We have the mare on our books at one hundred eighty," the timber boss said.

"Shaw, do that take in account the gears?"

"Contrary. We value the bridle, collar, check-lines, brichen, hames, and trace-chains, at $50.00. I am willing to consider the account settled if you will help me log past planting time."

"I'll let you know come Monday," Dad said, after he thought for a spell. "Either I'll bring the gray mare with me or I won't. If I don't bring her, you'll know we got a trade."

"Splendid. As you wish." The timber boss tipped his little derby hat and headed off for the low gap.

For the next two days Dad and Reek thought on the deal and figured. Reek must have used two extra boxes of snuff. It never lasted him long once he talked in a big way.

"Reek," Dad said, "you're doin a heap of writin and wipin."

"Shaw. I got me this number-eight hillside turner spotted. I could make a right smart of money, plowin for folks."

"Hell, come summer, you'll spend ever free minute you got, fishing." Dad muttered.

Dad never did say what he meant to do, but I noticed he looked close at the wagons and buggies sitting around the church on Sunday.

"Reckon we'll keep the mare," he said at breakfast that Monday morning. "You turn her out well after we leave--give her plenty of roughage so she won't fret so after the other horses are gone."

After Dad and Reek left with the others, I heard the mare whinny at daybreak. I fed her a bundle of tops and some fodder. By late morning she'd quit braying like a jackass.

"I'm glad she shet her fool mouth," my younger sister said. "Maybe now them old dogs'll hesh."

"You better quit talking like that," I said, "Mama'll take a limb to you."

"Mama washed her mouth out with soap last week." My older sister said, which started a fuss. They ran around the table slapping at each other.

I never knew who named the mare; we just all called her Sally. Dad and Reek stayed on with the logging company after planting time passed. Over time, Dad got hold of a wagon, single-foot, twister and a layoff plow. A while later he added a one-horse mowing machine and hay rake.

With Dad and Reek gone off to work, not much farming went on that summer. Ceece and I rode Sally over to the Frog Eye Hole in Junaluska Creek, where lots of people went to swim. We played cowboy and Indians as we went.

Ceece was a son of our closest neighbor. We run together most of the time.

Sally waded out into the water up to her waist and stood there for hours while we slid off her back into the water. Sometimes we dove off. Ceece, who was quite a bit smaller than me, walked up her neck and dove from her head. When he stood too long, Sally slung her big head, sent him high in the air. It tickled us to watch him flail his arms like a buzzard with a broken wing.

"Did you see that?" he said. "That horse tried to kill me that time."

No one paid any mind to him; he always ranted and raved about something.

Just before the sun went behind the mountain, Sally shook herself like a dog and headed for the bank. I tied her halter rope to a sycamore limb and played on. But without our slide, it was not much fun.

"I wanted to stay longer," Ceece said, right before he fell asleep leaning against me as we rode home. "Could have, too, if it wern't for that plagued, contrary horse."

Dad plowed Sally without lines. At "Come up," she walked closer to the row. "Come here," and she'd walk more in the middle. "Come around," at the end of the row and she would turn without stepping on a single plant. "Hold right there," and she stood, on the hillside, without letting the hay rake or mowing machine back up an inch.

I spent much of my time with her. Every evening I led her and our milk cow down the road to graze along the branch.

Saturday following a bad winter storm that washed out the road all the way to the mouth of the cove, Dad led Sally up to the house. "The weather's so bad the truck wouldn't make it to town." He draped a bushel of shelled corn across her back and tossed Ceece and me on top of the corn, and lead off toward town.

"I'd rather ride the truck," Ceece said. "This old fodder burner is too slow."

"Maybe," Dad allowed, "but she don't bust her tires on the washed-out road."

We got there before the mill opened. Dad threw the corn on the porch and we headed for the feed store. The feed store had a rich odor of stock feed, which pleased my nose. Dad stayed there until he caught up on the price of livestock and the gossip in the valley. Later he went off to the poolroom, while Ceece and I made a dash for the picture show. As always, we saw it twice before I could get him to leave. Even then I had to promise we'd buy us a pouch of tobacco. We slipped out in the alley and smoked until we got sick. Ceece slept all the way home, leaned against me on Sally's back.

A short time later, Dad seemed troubled. Grandpa had took sick. We tried to go see him every weekend, but he lived way over in Hardslate Gap, and our old truck was falling apart. Some trips we had to stop three or four times just to pump up the tires. We couldn't buy new tires because of the war; ration stamps never seem to make it this far back in the mountains. We kept a wet rag wrapped around the fuel pump to get the truck to go up a hill.

Once we had to hire a taxi, even. "It run me might near a week's wages," Dad told Grandpa. "Don't make sense, you here and us no way to get to you." After much pleading, Grandpa agreed to come stay a week or two with us.

The very first evening we all walked out onto the porch. Grandpa scratched his beard and looked off to the mountains. "I'd better get back across the hump."

This meant yet another trip in the old truck, but Dad knew it was either that, or the old man took off walking for home. This happened twice more before late summer.

One evening in early fall, two men came up the cove in a black roadster, with Georgia plates. It sure was a pretty thing, with its shiny brass hood ornament and all.

"I'm looking to buy a logging horse." The driver said, as he hung the gourd back on the hemlock limb above the spring; he kept looking at Sally up on the hillside.

"Hadn't thought much about selling her," Dad said.

"I've bought a boundary of timber, down next to Gainesville," the man said. "I need the horse."

"Shaw," Reek said, while he rubbed the hood of the car with his hand. "The big loggin companies done cut everything big enough to whoop a dog."

"Would you be willing to sell her?" the man said.

"No, I believe not."

"I'll come right to the point. I need the horse, but I don't need the car." The man said.

Dad and Reek looked over the car. Close. They spent a long time rubbing the tires. After a couple hours hard trading, we ended up with the roadster.

"It's a God-sent," Mama said.

I felt bad seeing Sally go, but kept it to myself.

"I guess this is the first car ever to come to the cove, regular like." Dad said, as he wiped the road dust off the car's fenders. "Once winter sets in bad we'll leave it down at the forks."

Reek took off his hat and scratched his head: a notion had struck him. I thought he had come up with something wrong with the car we hadn't seen. "Shaw! Where will a body haul their dogs?"

Mama wrapped two of my sisters and me in a quilt and put us in the rumble seat when we went to see about Grandpa.

Dad talked of buying a mule come spring-- pointed out that they eat a lot less than a horse. I knew he was right, and I liked the car. Still I missed the big gray mare.

Come the next spring our sow gave birth to a big litter of pigs. Little gray colored creatures, with a million little spots, scampered all over the sow.

They looked like ants in a nest, climbing all over the bed, Reek had made for them.

Three times, Reek counted on the fingers of his left hand. "Shaw, she cain't set the table fur'em all."

"You're right," Dad, picked up the runt and looked it over. The pig squealed and squirmed like it was about to die.

"I'll tend to it," I said. "The cow's giving a lot more milk than we can use."

"It's a boar pig," Dad said.

"Shaw," Reek said. "He's so little you'll have to tie a knot in his tail to keep him from fallin through the cracks in the floor."

I took the little pig home, made him a bed out of an old kindling box and sat it by the cook stove, and fed him with a doll bottle my oldest sister gave me.

"Cain't say I like the idea of a pig living in the house," Mama said. The next day, I saw her holding him in her arms and feeding him.

That first week, he had good life about him, but didn't seem to grow. I fed him on a sugar tit made from a piece of bed sheet and cane syrup.

"You can put him back in the pen now," Dad said, "the sow laid down on two of her pigs and killed them. His mother's milk might be better for him."

I looked at Mama.

"He'll do fine, here. . . ." I saw by the look on her face this was not going to happen. "The sow might not accept him. Even if she did, she might lay down on'em."

"If it don't start growing soon," Dad said, "we'll have to take the chance."

The next week the little fellow started to grow. He might not be as big as the others but he grew fast as a weed. His color changed, too, to a burnt brown.

That year we had enough corn left over to feed some of them, so Dad sold only part of the pigs after they were ten weeks old. As always, Mr. Seth Vest got the pick of the litter.

"I'll sell'um as shoats," Dad said. "They'll bring a better price that way."

I listened for him to say something about the pig in the kitchen. From the look on Mama's face I knew she'd let Dad know if she wanted something done with him.

It fell to me to pull weeds every day for the hogs, and that house pig followed every step I took. One day he rutted over the milk bucket. Before Mama came out of the garden, I cleaned up the mess and built him a lean-to outside the kitchen door. "You've lost your warm place, boy," I said, "You'll never get back in Mama's kitchen."

Mama caught him a few evenings later, he had pulled half a row of young turnips in her garden.

71

She broke a limb off the hedge bush and went after him; caught him by the ear and thrashed him good. I tried not to laugh but my youngest sister cackled like a hen that had just laid her first egg.

"You two re-plant them turnips--and mind that pig." Mama said, as she passed us, going back through the kitchen door. Getting whooped worked better on him than it did on us kids. We never saw him go near the garden again.

Ceece did not like to take Pig along when we went to the woods to play, and one day I caught him throwing rocks at it.

"You stop rocking my pig!" I yelled.

"Why?" He let another boulder fly.

"Cause if you don't, I'll rock you till you yell calf-rope."

Ceece let another rock fly. It hit the target, and the pig squalled and backed up in a brush pile.

I picked up a handful of dirt clods from the skid trail and threw some at Ceece. He threw a rock back at me.

I got mad. Went straight at him, showered him with dirt clods. He ran down toward the cove road. Stopping to ford the creek, he set sail another rock that barely missed the pig. I cut down on him with another handful of dirt clods; stung his back bad enough that he started to cry.

It was three days before he came back down to play. Neither of us, ever, said one word about the rock throwing. But the pig never forgot. Every time Ceece came near it, the pig growled at him like a dog.

Later Dad sold the other shoats. My pig was bigger than any of the others, but he never let on like he would sell him, even though I knew he would have to sooner or later.

In mid-summer, a farmer walked up into the yard. "I heard you got some young hogs for sale,"

"Sold'um day-a-fore-yesterday," Dad said.

The man pointed to Pig. "What about that funny-colored'un?"

"He ain't for sale." Dad said. "That'ens our yard hog."

The farmer grunted and walked back across the creek without so much as a fair-ye-well.

Come late summer the pig was nearly as big as his mother. I had to let the dog collar he wore, out every few days. He was real muscled up from running loose and tagging after me.

"Come hunting season, we'll have to pen him up," Dad said. "Else the dogs might kill him."

"The woods are full of wild hogs," Mama said. "Him being a boar, he might try to run with them. Think about it."

I didn't want to put him in a pen, though he'd done and killed three chickens, which I buried without telling. Nor did I want to see him butchered. Which I knew would come one day.

"I'm gon'na take him to the county fair in Prospect." I said one night, while I dried Mama's dishes. "Win me a ribbon like my sister does with her can goods."

"Then what?"

"Sell'em."

Later, Mama told Dad what I had said, he thought on it for a good spell. The next day he told Reek, who for once didn't have no fast answer. He just leaned forward and spat snuff off the porch.

"That hog don't look like no Pole and China, like the rest of them pigs." Dad said.

"Shaw. For a fact." Reek tapped the end of his snuff can; something he always done to get the snuff away from the lid before opening it.

"I hate to sell him," I said. "I don't have no choice."

"Well," Dad said to me, "if that's what you want to do."

"Shaw. He ain't a bad lookin hog. Sort'a on the skinny side."

Dad looked me in the face. "Most of the hogs at the fair will go well over four hundred pounds."

"Shaw, I'll say. Some seven or eight," Reek said. "Even a thousand."

"Really," I said.

"Shaw, sell his snout. Hit's so long he can eat the guts out of a pumpkin through a knot hole in the fence."

Dad put his hand on my back. "You'll see a bunch of high dollar hogs at the fair."

I started to get Pig ready. I changed his bed every day and led him down to the creek for a bath every other day.

"He won't render out enough grease to dirty a skillet." My older sister said, when I made her help me sprout corn to make mush to feed Pig.

I knew fat was what made a hog worth money. I fed him all the shorts and cracked corn he could eat. He grew longer and put on weight, but not much fat.

"You and Reek better build him a good crate," Dad said, the next evening. "Them judges look at the crate as well as the hog."

The next morning, soon as it was light enough to see, I started rounding up what saw mill slabs I could find. By late evening I had a crate of sorts. The next day I painted the leather hinges black with wood ashes and lard, to make them look like metal.

"It looks fair to middling, considering ...." Dad said, "you cain't make a race horse out of a jenny."

"Reek," I said, "I've oiled Pig's skin. Still, he don't have a shine."

"Shaw, you need some coal. Hit'll make his coat shine, like a brass door knob."

I left for the railroad track, after I done my feeding the next day. Three hours later I was back with a toe sack half full of coal. I rubbed the hog four times the next day with the coal, but I couldn't tell it helped him much.

"Shaw, boy, don't rub the coal on it, feed it to him."

Pig ate the coal like it was candy and his skin glowed like a wet rock. I scratched his back. "You may not be the fattest pig there, but at least you'll out shin'em."

Mama had me help string and break beans the next Friday. I held a fruit jar up against the sun to see if it was clean. "I reckon Dad and Reek thinks taking Pig to the fair is a bunch of foolishness," I said.

"Reckon so." She stuffed beans in a jar, and never looked up.

"The fair ain't a week and a half away,"

"You're right about that."

The day came to take Pig. Dad got up early and took the truck up the cove.

"If he gets to talking to Reek, they may go fishing," I said, while we ate breakfast.

"Possible," Mama said.

"They ain't a comin back," my younger sister said. "That old hog ain't got a chance, no how. You ain't got the sense God gave a goose, you'd make more pickin huckle berries with me, on the halvers."

I went down to the spring to get away from her and that mouth. Not long after that, I heard the truck, coming down the cove. On the back sat a crate made of peeled pine poles, notched just like a house. It even had a window and a split-board roof. Reek had made a trough from a hollowed out poplar log.

"Shaw, I just want that little pig to look re'specta'bule," Reek said, when I tried to thank him.

I walked off wandering where Reek got that word.

The county fair was the biggest thing that went on in these parts. They held it at the school, and folks filled every room with can goods and crafts. Indian women brought in their baskets and woven blankets. Out in front there were piles and piles of hickory handles, to fit everything from a shovel to a bark spud. Most folks hewed crossties to sell to the railroad, or split locust stakes, if they could find the time and timber. It was the only folding money they saw all year. Old man Nations had over a thousand ax handles in one pile. In the rear sat the biggest shed in these parts. Outside, the grassy flat was covered with small sheds and tents, all the way to the river.

"Foolishness," Dad said as we passed the midway.

I don't see why the rides galled him so. They only have a set of swings and merry-go-round.

By early evening we had everything unloaded and put out for show.

"Reek, where you been?" Dad said.

"Shaw, I been tradin knifes. Now I got me three." He held out his handful of knives. "And ever one of 'um better than the one I brung."

"You always could out-trade these city folks," Dad said. "You're the plug knife king."

"I'll feed your hog for you," a man walked up to us. "Fifty cents a day."

I had known all along that Pig would be here four days, but had not give any thought once about who was going to tend to him.

"You feed him for two days," Dad handed him a dollar. "We'll be back then."

I didn't say a word, but I grew more uneasy about Pig and his chances. The best I could hope for was some farmer might buy him, once the fair was over, or I might just turn him loose to run wild.

We got back two days later, the number of live-stock had grown into the hundreds. And maybe twice that many chickens.

"Pig ain't got the chance of a snowball in hell," I said, to Dad, when I found him watching a tractor go round and round.

"Watch your mouth," he said. "What do you mean? I warned you, there will be some fine stock here."

"Right under that big sign, there's a hog weighs nearly a thousand pounds," I said. "That's why."

We stood and watched the tractor. They'd tied the steering wheel to a one of its fenders, so the tractor went in a tight circle. It had already cut big deep grooves in the ground.

"I never said it would be easy," Dad said as we walked back toward the sign that read SWINE SHED.

As day broke, a man and two fat boys walked down, the open space between the crates, looking at every hog. I had them figured to be the judges at first, but the boys was no more than four years older than me. The man looked at Pig and turned to the boys. "Some of this stock's been shoved away from the feed trough."

"I wouldn't bring nothing to show," one of the boys said, "that looks that stunted."

A while later the boys set on a red crate, with a hog inside that was mud fat: couldn't see its eyes. I slept that night on a tobacco basket full of toe sacks I found in the truck. As the sun broke through I rubbed the sleep out of my eyes and went to the creek to wash my face and get some water for Pig. Later I toted water and washed him again.

By mid-morning the three judges had gone halfway down the other side. Why, if they asked me a bunch of questions, I'll die. What if they said? "Take this hog home and feed him." As for Pig, he looked worse to me every time I looked, but still I brushed him.

"Interesting," one of the judges said, once they made their way to us.

"Bacon type," another said. "Getting popular in other places."

"Not here," the third added.

I climbed up on the crate and wished Dad would come soon. The judges left the shed a little while later. Pig looked at me like I ought to go get him some more feed.

"Reckon we'll take you home and peddle you out come cold weather," I told Pig. "Cain't turn you loose to run wild, you'd starve."

Then I saw a judge coming back. He walked fast now, held a red ribbon and looked at the numbers on the crates.

"Your hog, son?" he checked his papers.

"Yes sir."

Was they go'na to do something to me and Pig, for him not being as fat as the others. I'm doing all the worrying and all he done was grunt, that silly half-hog, half-dog grunt, like he was hungry. "Bruink."

"What is your name?"

I could hardly speak, but I told him. He wrote it down on the papers, then pinned the ribbon on the crate.

I jumped back up on the crate. Some hog owners came by to look at my hog. I fretted, while I waited for my folks to get there. The man and fat boys walked by like their hind-ends had been set a fire. They didn't look my way.

"I'll go later and see if they got a ribbon." I said to Pig, low enough that nobody could hear.

"Come see!" my baby sister said from behind the crate. "We got ribbons all over our things. Won money, too."

"Where's Dad and Mama?"

"Mama's playing bingo. I don't know where Dad went."

I followed her into the school. Ribbons hung on lots of their stuff, even some blue ones.

"Lookie here," one of my older sisters said. "I won me twenty-five dollars on this crocheted bedspread."

It was the best of all nights. It was ten-thirty before we gathered up to go home.

"Want'a stay with your hog?" Dad said. "Folks who win ribbons are supposed to leave their things here till tomorrow night."

"I'll stay."

Folks brought livestock before daybreak. Chickens, dogs, cows, mules and the like were tied everywhere. It was the biggest trading day of the year in our county. At 7:00 a log truck drove in with a big gray horse standing on the bed, the gears hung loose from its lanky frame.

"Holy cow. . . .That looks like Sally!" I said.

I'd never saw the man before that backed the truck up to the loading dock. I ran over before he got his door open. Up close, there was no doubt in my mind. The gears were worn out. She had a galled place where the collar rubbed, she was thin as a rail, but it was Sally all right. I watched the man unload her. She seemed sound, except her weight and the fact that she was barefoot and had been that way a long time. Not even one nail hole in her hoof. I rubbed her big head.

"Want to buy a horse, boy?"

"How much you asking?"

"Two hundred dollars, and I'll throw in the gears."

It might as well of been two thousand. I turned and walked back to my crate. This time, I sat so I could see the horse. People came by and bragged on my hog, until I forget to go to the midway for something to eat.

About 4:00, in the evening, two men come into the shed. They dressed a little different from most folks; had on caps--not hats like most mountain men wear.

"How much you want for the hog?" one of them, said.

"I ain't had no notion of selling him." I said.

"We have a hog farm just outside Greenville," the man said. "We've been looking for a bacon-type boar such as him."

"Hadn't figured on selling him."

Now the other man started in. "Make him an offer."

"Okay, I'll give you a hundred dollars for him."

My thoughts run a mile-a-minute. I never dreamed a hog would bring that kind of money. I sure hope Dad and Reek shows up. . . . Soon.

Now I had to give these men an answer. "I don't know. . . ."

"Did you raise him, son?" The older man said. "If you sell him around here, he'll be butchered."

"I still ain't sure . . ."

"We're going to have to leave soon," one man said. "We'll give you a hundred and forty, for crate and all."

I looked around one last time for Dad and Reek.

"All--right."

The older man counted out the money while the other one brought a new truck around. We skidded Pig and the crate up on their truck. In a few minutes they were gone.

No more than five minutes later, I saw Dad's truck turn in at the gate. Not having a wallet, I held the money in my hand and ran to tell them what had happened.

"What do you think of this for a high-dollar hog, Reek?" I stuck the money up in his face.

"Shaw, shaw, shaw," Reek said with a big, snuffy, grin.

"That long hog will make them fellows a good boar," Dad said.

"Shaw. I suspicisioned hit all along; that hog's mixed up with the wild hogs in some way. What made him so long."

"Where in this world did you come up with that five dollar word." Dad said.

If Reek heard, he never let on.

"Dad, a man brought Sally here to sell," I said. "He wants two hundred dollars."

"Well now, son, you know we can get our plowing done cheap, by that Shope boy with his mule."

"I know."

"Want to try and buy her back with your money?"

I looked down at the sheaf of twenties I was still holding. Somehow it never dawned on me, that I'd be keeping all of it.

"Let's go look at her anyway," I said.

We looked her over for a spell. Just about the time we got done, the owner came over, none too solid on his legs. He had a pint bottle stuck in his hip pocket.

"This horse for sale?" Dad said.

"And a damn good loggin horse she is, too," Sally's owner said.

"Shaw," Reek run his hand across Sally's back, "She looks like a stack of cracklins. She ain't et in a month of Sundays."

"What you asking?" Dad said.

"One hundred seventy-five. Harness and all."

"Shaw. For this plug?"

"They ain't asking but nine hundred for that brand new tractor." Dad said.

Reek shook his head. "Shaw, that horse is so old it can eat peanuts out of a soda water bottle."

I couldn't count all the times I'd heard Dad and Reek bargaining down for something, but I never saw them tear into anybody like they did now. Was it because Sally's owner was drunk? Was it because he had treated the mare like he had?

"She's a good horse to the plow," the man got to say something.

"And poor as a snake," Reek ran his left hand across Sally's ribs. "I can count her ribs from way over yander; they stick out like tater ridges."

"I'll take a hundred and fifty," the man said. "Hell's bells, there ain't no logs left anyway. Acid wood don't fetch nothin, no-how."

"Shaw, we ain't about to haggle over this pile of chitlins," Reek said. "We'll give you a hunnard and twenty."

Reek turned and started to walk off, like he was mad. Even I couldn't tell if he was or not. Nor even if we wanted the mare, the way he'd talked about her.

"Okay," the man called when Reek was forty feet or so away. "You don't intend to let a body live."

In a few minutes we had Sally loaded onto our truck. "Me and Reek are some good hog and horse traders," I said, as we turned toward home.

"By the time you buy a set of shoes, a new collar, and enough sweet feed to fill her out, you'll be dead broke," Dad said.

"Shaw, what a way to talk to a young horse trader."

"Will Ol Sally still whinny when she hears the front door shut?" I said, to Mama, as we eat the next morning.

"You never can tell." She said. "Don't think so."

I gulped down my breakfast, and started for the barn. Sally whinnied twice, before I crossed the creek.

"She's not calling you to the barn!" Dad yelled. "She's telling you not to slam the blamed door so hard."

MOSES WALKINGSTICK --- THE HEALER

The first time I ever saw Moses Walkingstick was the day Harrison got hurt. Several of us boys were roofing a corn crib for Mr. Seth Vest, on Pounding Mill Branch. We had worked all summer, cut tobacco all the way from Hanging Dog Creek. Now we were doing this roofing job up near Granny Squirrel Gap.

Around mid-day, Harrison jumped off the roof onto a pile of old boards and ran a rusty spike up through his foot. It was half as thick as a railroad spike and it came all the way out the top of his boot--stuck up through the laces about two inches.

Harrison was only twelve years old but he was already on public works. He stayed with our family while he picked up jobs hereabouts. He was from over in the Cowflats Section. Only a few families lived that far back, where the land is too steep to clear. What work there was that high up was in timber, and logging camps wouldn't hire no one under the age of fourteen. War jobs never reached our mountains, even though the war had been going on for some years.

I thought for sure Harrison would pass out as Mr. Vest pulled the spike out of his foot. He never cried one tear or whimpered once. I would have cried--most likely screamed my head off. He did throw up in the weeds where he lay a little while later--trembled all over, even his face. We all gathered around to look at the wound, after he got his boot off. Only a few drops of blood dripped from the bottom. I saw this black hole in his foot, covered with a mix of rust and blood. Beads of sweat as big as saucers covered his ghost-white face. I felt his pain in my belly.

Harrison hobbled the rest of the day. Mr. Vest put him to pulling nails so he wouldn't have to be on the foot so much. He limped so bad by supper time, he could hardly make his way up on the porch. After we ate, his foot hurt him something fierce--no way could he get any ease. I saw a red streak running up by his ankle almost clear to the knee. We took turns rubbing his foot, trying to ease the pain some, but if it helped any, I couldn't tell. I saw the torment in Harrison's face.

"A wound that don't bleed to clean itself is hard to heal." Mama said.

Dad wanted to give him some white whisky to ease him off some. It took courage to ask her, but Mama poured out a half-a-teacup, from the bottle Dad brought from the corn crib. She used a splinter from a stick of stove wood as a wick to burn the alcohol off the liquor.

"When you do that, woman, you do away with everything that's good in it," Dad said while we watched the bright blue flame dance above the cup. "For sure the pain-killing part just went up in smoke."

His words faded like the flame as the alcohol burned off. Mama turned the handle on the sieve like she had to get the flour ready for supper right then and now.

We put Harrison in a chair in front of the fireplace and built a fire even though it was still early fall. I sat beside him for a spell but we neither one felt like talking.

I helped Dad, when he went to the shed for his cobbler's tools and fixed the boot. Dad had a worried look on his face. He pulled the boot off his shoe anvil and handed it to me. "Take this to the boy. It may make him feel better, to see the new sole we'd put on."

"It may be a long time before he needs this boot," I said.

"Maybe never."

"You don't mean he could die?"

"I mean just that. Or else loose that foot."

Mama fixed up a wash-pan of water with turpentine spirits and salts. Harrison, with teeth clenched, put his foot into the water. I showed him the boot and turned my face toward the wall to keep from crying, as he looked it over.

We turned on the radio to take Harrison's mind off the pain. We only listened to the radio at news time and Saturday nights if we could get the Grand Ole Opry to come in. Batteries are scarce and costly. We tried everything we knew but nothing seemed to bring him any peace.

Several folks living nearby come to see if they might be of any help, bringing food, just like they did if they came to set up with the dead. Others came out of curiosity. By nightfall the house was full. Everybody had some advice to pass on, or some warning to deliver. There was a lot of talk about lockjaw.

"Hit's the worst death there is," an old man said, loud enough for all to hear. "I seed a man with it once; his face was all out of sorts when he died. Like this." He twisted his face with both his hands.

It would have been funny if Harrison had not been in so much pain, and so worried. I saw the talk got to him, moreover the lockjaw stories. Mama's black eyes stared at them with a furry that made me tremble; she bit her lip until I looked for the blood to gush out. Dad led the men-folks out into the yard just in time.

There was a doctor in town, an educated man, who always wore one of them white shirts with buttons on the side. Some said he did good work, but didn't take his doctoring to heart. Everybody knew he liked money and had a taste for women and bonded whisky.

His place was above the feed store. He'd spend all afternoon shooting rats in the alley behind his office, fired down on them from his window with a 30-30 rifle. When he did manage to hit one, there was nothing left but a hole in the ground. Still, he'd tear out down the stairs to confirm his kill. By early evening he'd be drunk.

At dusk Dad walked over to where Mama stood. "I'm a go'na go where I can use the telephone." I heard him whisper to her, "I'm going to see if I can round up the doctor."

Not that the doctor had a phone in his office, but the telephone operators worked out of another office above the dry goods store. A body had to call the operator, who'd walk down the hall if she had a free minute and fetch the doctor to the phone. This late, they'd have to send the law to fetch the doctor.

Dad got back a while later and he walked over to where Mama, stood listening to Mrs. Babbs. "Never mind about the doctor--operator says he went to a convention down in Chattanooga. My guess is he's over at the Terrace Park Hotel, drunk. So I sent word for old Moses Walkingstick to come and do what he can."

I'd heard many a story about Moses. How he never gave up long as a sick person showed any signs of life. Once Moses rode over a hundred miles on a logging train flat-car. He held a death grip on the stub of a man's leg, which was cut off right above the knee. Kept him alive until they reached the hospital.

"I declare, what does that old Indian know about medicine?" Mrs. Babbs asked almost, before the words got out of Dad's mouth.

"It's a crying shame they gave that Indian a Bible name like Moses," another woman said.

"Once I took sick with the new-monie fever and that Indian sent over some boneset tea for me to drink," Mrs. Babbs said, for all to hear. "When I took the stopper out of the vial, it smelled so bad everybody thar took sick to their stomachs."

"It's plain you didn't die," Dad said under his breath. "Least-wise, your tongue's still working."

"Now, you take that doctor in town," Mrs. Babbs went right on without paying any mind to Dad, "he's got the sweetest-smellin medicine. Hit makes a body feel the best."

"Sugar syrup and alcohol," Dad said, "Bet the stuff's a hundred and eighty proof."

"Why, I believe some of the potions that Indian carries in his bag is pizen," Mrs. Babbs said. "He won't tell a body what it is he doctors with. Bunch of yerbs and sech is my guess."

Dad slipped over between me and the fire. "She ought to know," he whispered. "She's got about ever ailment known to man--puts a lot of stock in them little sugar pills. Ever month she comes home from town with a double handful."

At 10:30 we heard a faint knock on the door. The dogs didn't bark out a warning. Not even Speck nor Lead growled.

Dad answered the door. A very small, very wrinkled Indian man with a scraggly gray beard followed him into the room. He had on a brown derby hat and carried a big skin bag over his shoulder. He moved quiet as a whiff of smoke through the woods; I couldn't hear his footsteps even five feet away. His coal-black eyes seemed to see everything in the room, at one time. He had that smell of damp woods about him that men get from a very long camping trip. Being near him gave me the feel of someone from a far off place and a time long past. Not a word did he speak after he met Dad at the door. I felt an air about this little man, of knowing what to do and the grit to get it done.

Harrison's foot looked bad. It had turned black all around the puncture. The red streaks running up his leg were now much brighter, and three reached blamed near to his knee. As he pulled the foot up out of the water, using both his hands, I saw the hurt and fear in his face.

Moses hunkered down by Harrison's foot, then took a snow-white piece of something the size of a small pencil from his sack. I couldn't tell if it was wood or bone. It might have been a rock of some kind--but I knew from the shine it had been handled a lot. He rubbed the end of it around and around the hole in the bottom of Harrison's foot. Ever now and then, he'd switch and use his forefinger.

The look on Harrison's face started to change.

"I put the wound to sleep," Moses said after he rubbed about thirty minutes. "Reckon the boy's asleep too."

I could barely make out his words from three feet away, and no one else paid any mind to them. Everybody stood around the room, jabbering about the weather and what-not. When they saw Harrison laid back in the rocking chair sound asleep, the looks on some of their faces softened.

"But," Mrs. Babbs said, "he'll wake up in an hour, hurtin worse than ever."

A while later Moses asked for some oatmeal. When a woman fetched it, he mixed it with some dry leaves from his bag, then added some strange-smelling liquid and mixed it in too. He took some wood ashes from the fireplace and cleaned the wound. Ever so heed-ful he placed the poultice on the bottom of the foot. On the top, he sprinkled some black powder he took from a cow's horn beaker.

As often happens when something was going on, I took the big-eye. Not being able to sleep, I kept the coffeepot going for the grown folks. Twice, I wanted to ask Moses about the lockjaw but the words wouldn't come out. I just fretted about it as the night wore on. An hour later everyone else was asleep around the room, their chairs leaned against the log walls.

Moses spent the balance of the night squatted down by the fire. How he kept his legs from taking cramps is beyond me. He never spoke. The only motion he made was when, ever so often, he felt of Harrison's foot. I know he never dozed, for he held a small clay pipe in his mouth the whole time, now and then he took a splinter from the fire and lit it.

Just before dawn broke, Moses took the poultice from the foot. He walked over to the coal oil lamp and studied it closely, then held it to his nose and sniffed several times. He muttered something to the poultice in Cherokee that was none of the words I've ever heard.

"See? Powder worked its way through the foot," Moses held the now dry oatmeal so I could see the traces of the black powder in it.

They were the first words he'd spoke since Harrison fell asleep hours earlier. He took one last look at the poultice and threw it into the fire.

Along about first light, Harrison woke up. He looked and acted like he had rested. Now, the red streaks only reached three or four inches above his ankle. He could do about anything with his foot without pain but wiggle his toes.

A neighbor who'd recently killed hogs had brought over a large mess of pork. Mama cooked Harrison a batch of brains and eggs, his favorite breakfast. He ate so much, some of the folks reckoned he was doing fine and they started for home.

A little while later some of us boys played ball out in the yard, with a hog bladder they had blown up and tied like a balloon. We kicked the thing back and forth.

Harrison hobbled along. He limped, but it was plain to see he took pleasure from the game.

"That boy dearly loves to play ball, do he not?" Mrs. Betty Bentley said as she readied to leave.

"Sure does," her man Frank said as they walked to the door. "Gets all out of sorts when they have to bring the bladder inside by the fire, to make it swell up again."

I was out back when Moses Walkingstick slipped out about mid-morning. Again none of the dogs barked. I wanted to know more about this little Indian that slipped so quietly into and out of our lives. I pondered on what he done for some time; I vowed to learn about yellow root, may apple, boneset tea, and the like. Life on a hillside farm has many risks and little money, so mountain people had to give a lot of time and study to sickness and injury. There was a longing inside me to learn more about this man and his ways. I knew that somehow I'd meet Moses Walkingstick again. Maybe then, he'd tell me about doctoring. His way.

A week later, while we ate supper, I asked about lockjaw.

"Shaw. Do hit look to you like his jaws are locked?" Reek pointed to Harrison, who chewed hard on a piece of cornbread.

We all laughed, even Harrison, who almost lost his food.

Harrison went home a week later. He had lost his limp.

"How's Harrison's foot?" Dad said, when we saw his mother down at the mill, some time later.

"Hit healed up the best you ever seed. Fact is, it didn't fester up a tall."

The next time I saw Moses Walkingstick was about ten months after Harrison hurt his foot. We were in town to sell some fryers we raised this spring.   The town was full of people, it being Saturday.

"How did the ballplayer's foot come along?" Moses asked as we came up to him.

"Fit as a fiddle." Dad had a big smile on his face.

The others walked on down toward the square, carrying the chickens.   I listened to a sidewalk preacher down on the corner.   Standing a half a block away, I heard him well enough.   That far away you could still hear if someone asked you something.   Anyone who got close would have the preacher take his text out on them.   That is if they didn't put money in his hat that he had laid upside-down over against the store front of Parson's Mercantile.

An old farmer limped up the sidewalk. He stopped and spoke to Moses. "I got a bad corn on my foot. Can you heal it?"

"Cain't heal corn," Moses said.   "I'll take a look. Shoe don't fit right. May can take corn off."

"Okay." The man unlaced his boot, right then and there.

Moses looked, then pointed to the porch in front of the Baily Hotel. The man climbed up, sat down, and stuck his foot out over the street. He had the biggest, ugliest corn on his right foot I ever seen-- bigger than a glass marble. Thinking of having to walk on that made chills run up my back.

Moses reached into his bag and took out a small black ball; it looked like he had made it from wax and oil. He worked it with his hands like a potter works his clay, then laid it down on the boards and took a pair of small ivory-handled knives from his sack. He wiped the shiny knives with a clean rag and laid them carefully on the porch so their blades stuck out over the edge. From his sack he took a large kitchen match, struck it and let the flame clean each blade.

Did he have in mind to just whack the corn off? Surely not.

Moses took the little black ball and worked it over the corn, as he did with the white thing, back in the cove. First he rubbed it back and forth, then around and around. After a few minutes the ball seemed to dry out, and I smelled an odor in the air like burning flesh, and coal tar.

Moses rubbed and rubbed. At first, the corn turned brown; a little while later it was almost black. Moses stopped rubbing and picked up the knives. With much care, he worked around the edge of the corn. In no time at all, the corn turned loose and he lifted it from the foot. All that was left was a shallow sunk-in place where the corn had been. No blood, not even any raw flesh. Moses dressed the foot with some salve, from his sack. My eyes were big as chestnuts.

"How much do I owe you?" The farmer said as he put his boot back on.

"Twenty-five cents," Moses told him. "If you got it."

The farmer paid and left.

"Couldn't tell him to get some larger boots," Moses said. "I suspect they're all he's got. He cain't buy more. Cain't even cut away the part caused the corn; with winter coming on."

Moses talked so much, I figured he must be upset. He packed up the knives; then I followed him on up the wooden sidewalk to the town square. Several folks had gathered near the southwest corner, away from the clatter of the preacher.

In the center of the crowd an Indian man was selling potions, tonics, and Bull Durham tobacco sacks full of herbs. He shined all over. His hair was oiled black as coal. A feathered headdress hung all the way down to his heels. Around his neck hung a big bear-claw necklace. He even had red and white beads on his moccasin boots. He had on so much toilet water I smelled him from way back in the crowd.

"Step right up, folks, get your medicines here!"

He took a bar of soap from his pile of goods and lathered his hands, as if he planned to wash up for supper. In place of rinsing them with water, he patted them dry with a towel.

102

"Finest soap ever made," he said while he wrapped the towel around his neck. "And I'm the only man knows how to make it."

He walked over to a wagon hub and took a hand full of axle grease and rubbed it all over his hands, like my sisters do when they make mud pies. In a few minutes, he poured some cold water into a pan and started to wash his hands. Lo and behold, the axle grease came off easy. Not a trace of the grease was left on his copper colored hands.

"Ain't that the most wonderful soap, ever been?" I asked Moses. "How you reckon he made it?"

"Just plain lye soap he packed under his nails and into his skin," Moses said. "The axle grease was on top of the soap, so when the soap melted, the grease just floated away with it. Works with any soap."

"How do you know so much about med. . . . "

I looked around and he was gone. Watching Moses walk down the dusty street made the feeling to know more about him come back stronger than ever.

About two years later; give or take a week or two, word came that old Cletis Long had broke his leg. They wanted some strong young men to go and help carry him out. Cletis was a very big man who lived way back up on Roaring Fork Creek. They asked me and Jimmy Rattler to come along and carry the lanterns, both of us being too young and puny to do much heavy lifting.

We loaded up in an old pick-up truck. The last rays of lights were leaving the highest peaks of the Smoky Mountains as we left the forks of the creek. The early fall weather was fair and we were able to drive within some three miles of the Long place. Everyone talked at the same time, like a gang of boys on their first night hunting trip. From the way the older boys talked, I felt worried. Mr. Long was such a big man we would not be able to get enough people around him to pick him up. The more they talked, the bigger he got.

From where we parked, we had to cross a big mud flat over a half a mile wide. Somebody had made a walk--way of sawmill slabs laid end to end. Some floated on the muddy water that smelled like rotten leaves and stuck to our feet like black glue.

Foxfire, what some calls Devil's Lights glowed on every rotting log and on the slabs like moonlight on water. The sun, let alone the moon couldn't shine through this thicket of willows and swamp gas. We tried not to step on it, for it seemed alive.

The gnats swarmed around the lanterns; every time I opened my mouth, I felt the little monsters go down my throat. Jimmy fell off the walkway trying to carry his light in one hand and slap the gnats away from his face with the other. He squalled like a river panther. "Ah-eeah-eeee!" Animal sounds broke loose from all sides, some louder than a freight train whistle. They made my skin crawl. After a long bunch of "What.....what....what wuz that?" we were quite as church mice, but we were sure traveling.

After we crossed the swamp, the land turned almost straight up. In minutes we climbed a steep ivy-covered ridge. The road was little more than a skid path, but we made good time, being young and wanting to show how much help we'd be, and a little scared.

We reached the Long place just after midnight. By the fire, sat Mr. Long with Moses Walkingstick by his side. Save for the wooden splint around his leg, Mr. Long looked fine. There was no swelling-- yet his leg had been busted for over thirty hours.

Moses pulled a rag from his leg. I looked close at the large blue-black place just above his knee. No doubt his leg was busted good, but there were no red streaks like I had figured. I smelled the turpentine as it dripped on the floor--that must be what kept the swelling down.

"Hello, Quill," Moses said to me.

It done me proud that Moses singled me out. I got the feeling again of being near someone from a time past.

Mr. Long weighed about 230 pounds, maybe more. We tried to figure out a way to lift him.

Given the far piece and the ground we had to cover, carrying him still looked beyond the bounds of reason to me. Perd Adams had the only plan. "All of us can carry him on his bed."

It was a big thing made of twisted ivy limbs, tied with twine and scraps of baling wire. It didn't look none to strong, and anyway it took two of the biggest boys to pick the thing up.

Moses went out toward the woodshed and came back with a big poplar board, about eight feet long and 18 inches wide. He signaled and Mr. Long worked his straight chair to the middle of the room. Moses put the board under the seat, which left both ends sticking out. Two of the Adams boys started to pick up the ends.

"Wait," Moses said, a little above a whisper.

He took another chair, turned the seat down and placed it over the board through the rungs. The backs of the chair stuck out like wheelbarrow handles. Perd took another chair and fixed the other end the same way. Now the carriers had good handles to work with. Moses put his hand on the chair Mr. Long sat in. "When go down hill shift to back of board. Make easy boys carry."

Moses took two belts and strapped the busted leg to the board tight enough so Mr. Long wouldn't slide off when we got to steep ground. Four boys carried the contraption whenever the trail was wide enough for them to walk two abreast. Mr. long used his good leg to steady himself and shift the weight if the toters slipped. When the toters wanted to rest or switch, they just sat the chairs down, which left Mr. Long resting in his chair on the ground.

"This thing works the best I've ever seen." Earl Sanders said, as he an another boy traded places without having to stop.

"Yeah," the boy said, "I'd it steal if there wern't one like it at every house you come to."

Mr. Long laughed, so I guessed he felt no torment at all.

Moses walked ahead of the lantern light as he led us down the mountain and across the mud flat. It was so dark I had trouble keeping my balance. This is the time of night that always seemed the darkest, the night creatures sound the most fearsome. I figured we'd bothered the varmints a plenty. It scared me so bad I had trouble keeping my legs from running.

We were all give out by the time we reached the truck. We sat Mr. Long in the truck bed, still in his chair. I looked at Moses--he didn't have a bit of mud on the tops of his boots, even though he'd walked out of the light most of the way.

"I'll pay you something directly." Mr. Long called to Moses. "When I can."

"You want one of these lanterns?" I hollered.

Moses didn't answer, he had already picked up the two empty chairs and was making his way back into the swamp. I knew Moses wasn't like ordinary folks, but it gave me a chill to think of crossing the mud flat alone without a light.

When the others asked questions about him on the trip back, it made me feel good. I liked the notice, and I liked to brag about Moses. Still, I didn't know much about him or his ways.

The hospital was all the way over in the next county. Mr. Long's leg hurt him while we were on the roughest part of the road but he got easy as when we reached the river road. There wasn't much talking on the way back, most of the others were asleep before we had gone halfway.

Day was breaking as we got there, but doctors were already at work. They x-rayed the leg while we stood around to watch. The doctor who done the x-ray told us he would snip off the rawhide and splints and put on a proper cast. But before he done any of that he called in another doctor.

"There's no swelling," he said. "It's beyond me how a break that bad could have been set that good without an x-ray."

"For the life of me," the other doctor said, "I can't see how it was done either."

A very old night nurse walked by and looked at Mr. Long's leg. "Moses Walkingstick must have been there."

I saw Moses again about a year later. One Sunday we were digging ramps over in the Winchester Cove. The little onion-like plants are the first fresh plants mountain people can get to eat in springtime. They only grow high up on the mountains, and only on the north side. They taste better than any tame onion and taint the breath worse than all the cloves of garlic ever grown.

"Shaw," Reek allowed, "most womenfolk don't cotton to ramps much."

"Mama eats one every time we have them at home." I said.

"Only in self-defense, she claims." Dad said.

"Shaw, hit's mixing them with white liquor that taints your breath so."

"You ought to know." Three of the men, said at the same time.

In Winchester Cove the pale green leaves cover the ground, mainly because ramp leaves are so much wider than an onion's. So at least twice every spring we menfolk made a day out of going to the ramp patch.

As we dug some large ramps up in the head of the cove, I saw a man making his way toward us. He moved real slow, his eyes were fixed on the ground as if he was studying it. It was Moses, of course. Reek had started frying potatoes by the time Moses crossed the branch. As he got closer, I saw his hands were full of roots and bark. The deerskin bag hung from his right side.

As he got even with us, we asked him to eat. Moses took with us a meal of ramps, cornbread, potatoes, fatback, and buttermilk. When we ate our fill, Moses took what grease there was left in his plate and rubbed it on his arms. I'd heard of old-timey folks doing this but had never seen it.

After we stuffed ourselves with every bite we could hold, we went over to a spring. Under the moss in the spring branch sat a frost-covered jug of home brew. It seemed to loosen up Moses's tongue. He didn't even seem to mind being asked questions.

"Shaw. Where wuz you raised, Moses?" Reek asked him.

"Over in the Snowbird Mountains. A woman name of Maude Cornsilk kept me til I struck out on my own."

"Where did you learn doctorin?" I said.

"From her, mostly. About the time I was ten years old they took me away to school--a far ways off, all the way out of the mountains. They never let us speak our Indian at the school, and the only English words I knowed was lard and cucumber. After school us boys went off into the woods and jabber our talk. I saw right off, it was better that I stayed at the school and learned more English."

Moses sat cross-legged in the warm afternoon sun. The feeling of wanting to know gave me a longing I only felt near this little man.

"Did you stay there long?" Dad said.

"When I was fourteen they let me go back and live with Maude Cornsilk. I could read a little; she had me read to her ever word she could find wrote down. Everything from snuff boxes to lard cans. I read most without looking after a while."

Moses got up to leave. Having always thought of him as being from a fore-gone time, I now realized he was also old. His face was lined like crow's tracks in red mud. His gait had slowed. Only, his eyes darted with the same brightness I'd seen before, as if a dancing blaze lit their coal-black depths. Moses thanked us for the meal and hobbled on up the mountain.

"Where's he a goin?" one of the men said.

"To my knowing there's no house or shelter of any kind for thirty miles in that direction."

"I've heard about some caves on the other side of the Nantahala River," someone said. "Bet that's where he's headed."

"Shaw," Reek said. "For a fact they hard to find in the dark. I been thar."

I grinned. I wasn't worried; Moses was at home in these mountains.

"How you reckon he knows to show up if somebody is sick or hurt?" I said after a long spell.

Nobody said anything, so I answered. "Guess he just feels it in his bones."

"Do you think his powers will go to the grave with him?" Dad said.

"Shaw, I reckon." Reek said, "he be one of a kind, he is."

Word came one day down at the mill that Moses Walkingstick was bad sick. For a long spell, nobody said a word. Maybe we were thinking about all the things Moses had done for people. Everybody had a story about him. Even though I knew more than anybody there; that wasn't saying a lot, and I didn't feel like talking.

"Where do you reckon he lives?" Someone asked Mr. Aaron Berry, who was the oldest one there.

"I'm not rightly sure. I re-co-lect somewhere up near the Weatherman Bald, on the back side, by the Walnut Springs."

"Let's tramp in there come the weekend," I said, to my younger cousin, Sunny. "We'll catch us a mess of speckled trout, lay out the night and hunt for Moses's place. I want you to meet him."

I didn't have to twist his arm. We hunted and fished together a lot. My wanting to see and learn more about Moses was far from over. "Let's do it soon."

"Day after Friday." He said.

Saturday, we left at daylight and tramped until late in the day. With me stopping and telling him tales, we hardly had time to catch us a mess of trout for supper. We made camp well after dark.

As the moon rose over the high waterfalls on Hurricane Creek, Sunny pointed toward the sky. "Damn my time a rainbow, what time is it?"

I dug my watch out and held it by the campfire. "Five-after-twelve."

"This is one hell of a place." Sunny stared at the mist filled air. "Lord help my time, I'll bet there ain't more'n a half dozen places on God's earth where a body can see a rainbow at midnight."

I thought of Moses and his strange ways. "I reckon as these mountains are full of wonderment."

Next day we looked for Moses's cabin. It was easy to find, seeing as how every tree for a quarter of a mile had something built in it. Little rows of herbs dotted the mountainside, most of them strange to me, though I did know catnip, bay root and lady slipper.

There was game, too, just about everywhere you looked. Three doe deer stood in edge of the laurel by the spring. Birds of every manner flew and hopped all over the place. There was hardly a tree that didn't have at least one squirrel's nest in it.

113

Sunny pointed toward the ridge that ran back of the cabin--there stood a sow bear and three cubs. "Never in my born days have I seen so many animals in one place."

"Guess critters need a little doctoring from time to time."

"We'll come up here huntin one of these days," Sunny said.

"Sure. One of these days," I said, even though I knew we wouldn't.

To call it a cabin was to glorify the shack we saw setting back in a grove of big hemlocks. Mill slabs had been nailed and tied together with rawhide to make the walls. The roof was slabs of tree bark and moss. On the north side, a chimney made of mountain rock stood straight and true. I had the same going-back-in-time feeling I'd had when I first saw Moses.

The minute I looked in the door, I knew nobody was there and, hadn't been in a while. "Moses! Moses! Moses!"

"You're wasting your breath." Sunny said. "Ain't been nobody here in a good spell."

I called and searched for the better part of an hour. Sunny took hold of my arm. "It's all for naught looking for him. It's plain to see, he ain't been here in months."

I knew he was right and followed him to the end of the house. He stood and stared at the chimney. "Look at the stonework on that chimney. Ain't it fine? Rest of the place is a dump."

"Moses has the best rocks in the world and nothing else." I said, while I looked for any sign of Moses.

Inside, I hoped to find a keepsake of some kind. In the back of my mind, I hoped to find the piece Moses used to put Harrison's foot to sleep or one of the ivory-handled knives, but the place was pretty well empty. Animals had been living there. On one side was a table that held a water bucket and a gourd. All around the wall hung herbs and roots; even this dry they left a sweet smell in the shack. On the other side of the room was a pallet. No other furnishings could I see.

I looked carefully around the room. I held the little gourd, like I was afraid I'd loose it. All at once, I spotted something white among the ashes in the fireplace. Sure enough, it was one of the knives. The handle was gone from one side, and the other side was burned black save for one little place. I rubbed the knife as careful as if it was gold; I gripped it tight and ran outside.

Sunny sat on a rock, leaned against the chimney, his eyes fixed on the stonework. "Bet old Moses sets here on cold days. Just like I'm a doin now."

I showed him the knife. "Where do you reckon Moses's at?"

"There ain't no telling, but for sure he ain't been here in a time and a time."

"Do you think a body ought to leave the knife?"

"Hell fire no. Them critters'll have this place wrecked in no time."

I went back inside for one final look--stood for a long time in the center of the room. A feeling that I was about to miss something kept coming back in my mind. While my eyes searched the cabin walls, floor, pallet, table--two or three times.

All at once I saw something on the roof line. There, behind some vines and roots, laying on the wall plate, was a book. A stub of a pencil wedged under it. I got it down. The pages were well worn and flying squirrels had chewed off the edges, but I could make out the title. Gray's Anatomy.

"Come on," Sunny called, "it's a gettin late."

I quit studying the little notes Moses had wrote in the book. I looked for a safe place to leave it but couldn't find one. With a blank page from the back of the book and the pencil, I wrote, "I have your book. Quill Vance." I placed it on the sill and covered it with a flat rock.

"Lookie here!" Sunny said.

I found him along another path leading toward the knoll behind the shack, staring at the ground. I was going to ask if I ought to keep the book.

"Look." He pointed at a rock standing on its end.

I stood for a long time just looking at the round mound of dirt that told us this was where someone was buried. I studied the rock; it had no carving or marking of any kind. There wasn't anyway of telling how long the grave had been there. The ground was too rocky and the weeds are dead this time of year.

"Reckon how old this grave is?" I said

I didn't dawn on me that Sunny had left, until he came back around the cabin carrying a board and a dogwood post. He sharpened the post, while I took out the little knife and carved on the board.

We headed for home. I had the knife in my pocket, the book under my arm. I took Sunny by the arm. "If anyone comes by upon this place, there'll have no doubt who lives here."

I looked back, one more time, at the sign Sunny placed in front of the cabin. Today, in my mind's eye, I can still see the carving.

THE HEALER.

AUNT NICA and the BIBLE BANK

"You know how she is," Dad said. "To poor to paint and too proud to whitewash,"

"She's a strong-willed woman," Mama said.

"Independent as a hog on ice."

"Resourceful as a body can be."

"She's so stingy," Dad fired back, "I'll bet she unwinds her clock at night."

The quarreling has gone on since supper, mostly good-natured; Dad had been hitting the rhubarb wine he kept hid in the smokehouse. I smelled it on him.

"She's your kin," Mama said. "At least go look at the furniture; Lord knows we need some."

"Cain't trade nickels with her." Dad belched more rhubarb. "She'll skin a flea for its hide and tallor."

They were still at it when I went to bed. I knew Mama always let Dad have the last word, but I knew we were at least going to look at the furniture. I hope they don't get into it so Mama's face has that hurt look or her chin quivers: them are the things I hate most in all this world.

Aunt Nica had sent word by the preacher that she wanted to sell some household goods. She told the preacher she would give Dad the rights to refusal.

We sure did need some, but we can only buy much of anything when our tobacco sells around the first of December. Most of that money goes for things like clothes and a few Christmas things. This year, it had rained a lot and the blue mold set the crop back more than two months. If it don't stop raining Christmas may be only a few oranges again. I'm sure the way he was talking had something to do with Dad not wanting to get Mama's hopes up.

The warmth from the wood cook stove, mixed with the smell of damp earth in the garden, made me sleepy even before the rain started on the roof. Next thing I knew, it was morning.

"Day after tomorrow, we'll be going over to Tater Town to look at the furniture," Dad said, the next day, as we shocked up some damp hay.

Aunt Nica had came to visit us once or twice every summer when Mama and Dad were first married. She had stopped before any of us kids came along. To my knowledge, none of us had ever been to her place. Tater Town was way back in the mountains, above Devil's Courthouse.

"Ain't nobody lives that far back," Dad said, "except folks dodging out from the law."

That night, I asked Mama if Aunt Nica was wanted by the law.

"Course not. She's you Dad's oldest half-sister, but they're about a generation apart in their ways."

That Friday morning Mama, Dad and I left, as soon as the feeding was done. Dad didn't rightly know just where Aunt Nica's place was; only it was somewhere in Tater Town. Mama wanted Dad to ask how to get there, but he wouldn't hear of it. Later on we ran straight into a herd of cows a man was driving down the road and Mama asked.

Then it took us until nine o'clock to find the place; set back in a bank that looked like the mountainside was about to swallow it. It was just a shack, no bigger than our can house. There was no porch, nor even a stoop covered the only door I could see.

I walked around the far side. It had only one small window, too high to see in. Dad pecked on the door, but there was no answer.

"You sure this is the place?" Mama said.

"I'm sure," Dad said. "Bet there ain't enough stuff in there to wad a shotgun."

Mama pointed up on the hillside to the right. "She might be at that barn up on the ridge."

"You wait here while me and Quill go see." Dad said.

The trail crossed a little branch, then climbed up a steep hollow. An old bathtub half full of water sat just off the trail, thirty yards below the sheds.

"She must have some livestock," I said.

Dad slapped the water with his right hand and grinned. "May be where she takes a bath."

"You durn tootin it is," said a little woman, as she came out of the biggest shed. She used a small walking cane. But what stood out was her apron. It had to be the biggest one I've ever seen. It looked like a bed sheet wrapped around her.

"Hello, Nica," Dad said.

"A body cain't a'ford to buy coal and wood to heat water," she said. "When I go to the barn in the morning, I lay that trough over in the branch. When I finish, the tub's half full. By the time I done my evening chores, the sun has het the water. I stop on my way home and have me a bath."

It all made good sense to me, but Dad shook his head, like he couldn't believe it. My aunt was a pint-sized woman, no taller than me. I had looked for her to be old, but once I heard her clear sharp voice and seen her dancing black eyes, I knew better.

"Is this the furniture you want to sell?" Dad said, once we got down to her shack.

I didn't see anything but some unmatched straight chairs setting on a dirt floor. A wood bedstead and a worn out eating table by the stove wasn't worth nothing but to make kindling.   We had more and better things in our bee house. Mama stood by the door with a hurt look on her face that I have only seen a few times. Still, I hate it more than anything.

Dad picked up one of the chairs.   "How much for a piece like this?"

Mama's chin quivered.   I hate that too.

"This hain't the stuff I sent you word about."

"Where's it at then?" Dad said.

"Down yander."

"Where?"

"Down at the new house. I'll show you."

Aunt Nica led us out in front of the shack.   She pointed down toward the main road with her cane. A quarter-mile almost straight down, I saw a rooftop. Two big white oaks blocked the rest of the house.

"Come on," Dad said. "We'll ride down in the truck."

"I hoof it every day, I do." Aunt Nica walked over to the edge of the bank.

The path followed a game or cattle trail that made it fairly easy going.   In places it was worn so deep in the hillside it looked like heavy equipment had been over it.

Aunt Nica led the way with the grace and speed even Dad had to hurry a bit to keep up.   The house sat back a good hundred feet off the main road.

The outside had lap siding and a dark gray shingle roof. In front there was a setting porch with a white rail. There were plenty of windows with drapes and a vine covered brick chimney. By far, it was the best house we'd seen all day.

I sat down in the glider swing; the white and green paint felt and looked brand new. Later, I followed them into the house. There was not a speck of dust or cobweb in sight. I walked to the fireplace and looked behind the screen. It was clean enough to eat off; no sign a fire had ever been built in it. No ashes or smoke stains anywhere. No smell.

The kitchen had running water and a Empire cook stove with a water jacket next to the fire box. A china cabinet filled with glassware stood against the wall. In the middle of the floor sat an oak eating table and six chairs, like the ones back in the cove. Only, ours was worn and scratched from all the cleaning and living.

What I didn't see was any sign that the place had ever been lived in. What puzzled me most was, the place didn't smell like it had been lived in nor did it smell like it had been shut up a long time. It didn't smell like nothing. It put me in mind of the playhouse Dad and Reek built for my sisters. They didn't want me touching any of their play purties, but they wanted to show them to me every day. I scratched my head. "Aunt Nica's house must be haunted."

Mama had a gleam in her eye I hadn't seen since my last baby sister was born.

"You can cook a meal and never leave the kitchen." She said

"Why don't you live in this house, Nica?" Dad said. "Or else, rent it out."

"Well, hit's like this here," Aunt Nica said. "My man give me his word that iff'en I'd marry up with him, he'd build me this here house."

"Seems like he done just that," Dad said.

"Not so. Hard times they overtook him, and I had to use my butter and egg money to finish hit. Told him right then and thar, I wouldn't never move here."

Not being able to put any reason to what she had said, we walked through the rest of the house. The pine wood floors shined from the oil and wax put on over the years. Mama looked over the furniture. I sat on the sofa; we've never had us a sofa couch. I hadn't seen one with arms before. No way could we ever go out and buy things this nice. I hoped and prayed Aunt Nica didn't want so much for her stuff that we couldn't at least buy Mama one piece. I don't want to see that look on her face or her chin quiver again. Ever!

Dad broke the silence. "Nica, your man's been dead fifteen years."

"Eighteen this Thursday past."

"Why don't you come live with us?"   Mama said.

"Naw. We moved so many times when I was a young'en that ever time the kitchen door opened, the chickens crossed their legs, thinking they were fixing to be tied up again."

After they talked for a spell, the furniture seemed to mean next to nothing to Aunt Nica, yet she seemed set on staying in Tater Town.

Then Mama come out with something that about knocked me back. "There's another baby on the way."   Dad must have known or guessed; at least he didn't have a running fit or nothing.

After a talk that lasted hours, it was settled. We would buy the furniture, and Aunt Nica would come live with us----at least for a spell.   I just hoped the new baby wouldn't be like my sisters.

It took two trips the next day to haul all the stuff. Dad went alone the last time, to bring Aunt Nica, while Mama and us kids straightened up.

"We have done and gone from a no-furniture place to over-furnished in one day."   Mama said. The look on her face, the best ever.

It was late at night, by the time they showed up. Aunt Nica came to the door with a 22 rifle in one hand and six shells in the other. Under her right arm was a big family Bible. "No way I'm a goin stay in no place sech as this without my 'tection," she said as she passed my sisters, who stood with their mouth's open.

The next morning Aunt Nica worked in the kitchen like she'd lived here all her life. She had on another apron that might have even been bigger. Any time one got soiled one bit; she put on another. By the time the mid-day meal was ready she'd changed it four times--my oldest sister kept count.

Every day, my youngest sister pestered me to go with her to smoke rabbit tobacco down behind the barn. She loved for me to hunt it with her, even though we had enough, hid down in the crib, to keep us sick for a month. She started in right after we ate. "Go get us some tobacky."

"Ain't hardly none of it left in the fields this late," I said. "There's plenty of real tobacco in the barn."

"I'll go you halvers," she said.

"I don't smoke that much, and it's hard to find this time of year, and besides how do you come off owning half what I go get?"

"If you don't go, I'll put pins in your bed. Anyway, it ain't hard to find if you go way back up in the head of the hollow, where the wind cain't blow it away."

I left right then for the weed patch--it was better than listening to her mouth all blessed day-long. You couldn't win any argument with that five-year old.

Dad smokes a pipe on Sunday and sometimes in the evening. A lot of mountain women used snuff and or chewed plug tobacco. Most tried to hide the habit; kept any stains off with a toothbrush made from a piece of blackgum wood. A few of the oldest smoked little clay pipes they buy from an old Indian up on Shuck Stack. Not Aunt Nica, when the supper dishes were done, she fired up a big cigar, looks like a piece of rope.

"Damn, that thing stinks, smells like a burning toe sack." Dad said.

Aunt Nica looked at him like he broke wind at the table. He was fixing to say something else when I saw Mama kick him on the foot. After a few days everybody cleared out as soon as they ate their meal. That is, except my youngest sister. She'd smoke anything.

"When does the rollin store run?" Aunt Nica said, at breakfast, a few days later. "You'ns do have a rollin store?"

"Tuesdays." Dad said.

"Well, glory be, that's day atter tomorrow."

"We don't meet it much."

128

"Pray tell, why in tarnation do you'ns go into town to trade all the time, when the rollin store brings it pert-near to your doorstep?"

"We trade at Miller's Mill, mostly," my oldest sister said.

"What for? Folks ought to go to town once a month to get their hard staples; the rest of the time you can buy off'en the rollin store."

Two days later, Aunt Nica lit out for the mouth of the cove. My youngest sister begged until I followed along. Because she wanted me to give her candy money, I figure.

The rolling store has once been a school bus. Its letters were painted over with whitewash, but on the side, where the door is, tree limbs had raked the paint off. You can still make out some of the letters. JACKS_____COUNTY SCHOOLS. The seats had been torn out and shelves built to the ceiling. I guess in time the stuff had been placed in them all neat like, but with our rough roads and people plundering, it looks like it was thrown in with a shovel. In winter it carried boots, overalls and a stock of dry goods.

"We don't buy our hard staples, here," Aunt Nica said to the driver as she climbed the steps. "Your price is out of this world."

"Yes sir," the driver said.

I started filling my jug from the barrel of lamp oil wedged between the back door and sacks of hog feed. The old pump thing leaked enough to give off a faint odor. Inside the old bus, it mixed with stock feed and cottonseed meal and gave the rear end of the old bus a smell like sweet oil.

"What aire you a haulin on the roof today?" Aunt Nica said.

"Same as always," The man said. "Shorts, laying mash, and horse feed."

"What you haulin on the back?"

"Not much, just some fryers and one pig."

Aunt Nica walked down the steps and around back where crates were tied over the bumper. The man raised the lids so'es she could see. I couldn't figure why she asked so many questions or wanted to see the chickens and pig--we had no mind to buy neither.

I got me a dope and pie and sat on the steps while Aunt Nica nosed and my sister prowled.

"Don't tell me the price of them cigars done and gone up again," Aunt Nica said. "They're higher than a cat's back now."

"No sir, they've been this price for several months."

"What's fresh eggs worth?" Aunt Nica said.

"Are you buying or selling?"

"Well, I declare. You aire a'aski. . . ."

"Three cent apiece," the man broke in. "Thirty cent a dozen."

"Aire they fresh?"

"Yes sir. Got them not a mile back."

She handed the man three pennies and picked up a big brown egg. I wondered what she wanted with an egg; we had plenty at home. My sister's eyes got bigger and bigger as Aunt Nica took a sharp-pointed piece of metal from her apron, and punched a hole in the end of the egg. She put it to her mouth and leaned her head back.

"Good Lord a'mighty!" I said.

"What in thunderation is she a fixin to do?" my sister said.

"Good gracious alive, she's sucking that egg," I said.

"Very good," Aunt Nica said, as she threw the empty egg shell out the door.

We started back up the cove road; I carried the coal oil and the poke of stuff Aunt Nica had bought. Aunt Nica had her cane and stogies.

My sister licked the candy from around her mouth. "I ain't go'na suck no raw eggs."

"Better for you than all them sweets," Aunt Nica said. "Or all that rabbit tobacky."

"Look, Aunt Nica," I said, as my sister skipped along. "She's a hoppin like a rabbit now."

I don't know if the rolling store man called everybody sir or just all men folks and Aunt Nica.

God knows she gave him reason to call her names. Then later on, when his bus broke down, he sent her a box of stogies by Dad, for free.

Another one that felt the wrath from Aunt Nica was Reek Moore. I figure it had to do with how Reek done in Mama's garden. Reek he sort'a grazes as he goes along, whether it's in Mama's garden or in the woods. When we were out hunting with him in the depths of winter, Reek fills his coat pockets with good things to eat.

To Aunt Nica this is next to a sin. "That durn old heathern knows a body's beholden to come to the table to do their eating. After they've washed up and said grace. Proper like."

"Reek, you give Nica a wide berth. Is it cause she climbs your case about all the time you spend in the woods, huntin and fishin?"

"Shaw, at thar old widder woman takes her half right out'a the middle."

A few nights later Dad hadn't got home and it was after dark. That didn't bother Mama none--he came home late a lot of times, when he had things that needed tending to.

Along about full dark, Aunt Nica got all fidgety and set in, every five minutes; she allowed. "Everybody knows, decent folks is at home a'fore dark, and rogues have got their sacks and started.

I'd give him a good currying if he was a man of mine."

Dad came in after she had gone to bed and left the next morning before she got up. Something to do with a neighbor's sick milk cow.

My sisters were playing in their playhouse one warm evening while Aunt Nica needed help to tighten the lids on some canning jars. She walked half way to the playhouse and bellowed like a bull. "Get your'n selfs to this house! Right now."

They circled the table in the can house and started taking on. "Why do we have to do all this canning for right now?" My oldest sister allowed, "it's a long time till cold weather and we've got fifty cans of beans left over from last year."

"When I get grown," my next to oldest sister said, "I ain't goin do no work."

"Well I ain't go'na do none now." My next to oldest sister said, "I'm sick; besides, I'll marry me a rich man." She thrashed around holding her belly and watched Aunt Nica out of the corner of her eye.

"When I was you'ens age I was a pilin brash," Aunt Nica said. "Til I couldn't move one foot a fore t'other."

"What's brash?" My baby sister asked everybody she saw for the next week. Must have asked me a hundred times. She asked Mama, Dad and

Reek one right after the other until I thought they would scream. Each one told her it was brush. It didn't matter; she asked the next one she met. "What's brash?" Even asked a woman down at the meeting on Sunday. Everybody told her the same thing, but she went right on. "What's brash?" I wish Aunt Nica had got me to help her; at least I wouldn't have to hear, again and again, "What's brash?"

"I wish that five year old would marry a rich man right now." I said to Mama that night.

She looked at me funny. She didn't have no notion of what I was talking about.

At night, after supper, it fell to me to see that there was enough stove wood for the next day. "No matter how much I cut and bring in," I said to Mama, "Aunt Nica burns it all."

I might as well have talked to a wall. "You haven't had to eat one cold meal, have you?"

It did give me a chance to watch Aunt Nica close. Aunt Nica cleaned the supper dishes, then reached down in her apron and brought out a little pouch of herbs. She sorted through until she found what suited her. Then she rolled them between the palms of her hands until they crumbled into an iron skillet. While they roasted, she sniffed the fumes. It smelled like burning weeds to me. Once they were to her liking, she took a rock and ground them up on the stovetop. When the seeds and sticks were beat to a powder, she brewed it into a tea.

"What's that stuff, stinking?" My oldest sister said.

"A layover to catch meddlers." Aunt Nica always said the same words when she figured any of us got nosy.

I couldn't stand the smell or taste of the stuff, but my youngest sister drank it like sugar water. She's got an iron stomach, I figure.

Aunt Nica was not with us all the time. Right before the first day of each month, she'd want to go back to Tater Town.

"I'll be a needin to get back to Tater Town come Friday. My benefit check is due to come in the mail."

"Your old age pension check," Mama said.

"Whatever."

Dad put on like he didn't mind taking her home one bit. But he let on like going to bring her back was wearing out his soul, mind, and body, as well as his truck. Me, I look forward to the tales she told about her trip.

"You look tired, Nica," Mama said, at the supper table, only hours after Aunt Nica got back from her next trip.

"What caused your milk to clabber?" Dad said.

135

Mama gave him a dirty look that ought to have set his skin afire. It lasted a long time, but he was in fine spirits and paid her no mind.

"I had me a bout with this Oat-see-mobile."

Dad like to have spit out his supper. "A what?"

"An Oat-see-mobile car. A thing with wheels like your truck."

"What in the world happened? Did you wreck? Were you kilt?"

Mama gave him a dirty look, but put her hand on Aunt Nica's arm. "Please tell us what took place."

"Well. Me, Virgie Mae and her man Ralph-- they neighbors, you know."

"How is we're supposed to know?" Dad said.

Mama gave him another dirty look.

"Iff'en you'd listen! You'd know." Aunt Nica said, "They had this Oat-see-mobile car, and hit weren't doing good. Well sir, we started over to Frank-o-land and the thing run hot, Ralph had to pull over. Scared Virgie Mae so bad she wrung a hunk out of her leg."

"I see. The Oldsmobile broke down on the way to Franklin." Dad said.

"That's what I jest told you," Aunt Nica said. "Ralph had to tote water in Virgie Mae's pocket-book to cool the blessed thing off."

"Then it was all right," Mama said, real quick.

"Lord-a-mercy no. We got the thing to the car lot in Frank-o-land, and the man where Ralph bought it, he told us to go all the way to Brushy Creek and get us a used radiator. Me and Virgie Mae, we couldn't figure out what that wuz, and Ralph he wouldn't talk about it."

"Did that fix it?" Dad said.

"Shucks fire no. Hit got hot and quit a'fore we'd gone more'n three miles."

"What'd you do then?" I said, so Dad wouldn't say something and get another dirty look.

"Virgie Mae wus a crying and a wringin her hands. A man come by and said he'd take his truck and go to the car lot and tell the owner. He did, and the car lot man brought his wrecker; hauled us and the Oat-see-mobile back thar."

"Then you got it fixed?" Dad started to get up.

"Naw, better still, he give us this t'othern and hit runs the best you ever seed. Ralph's pay dues didn't go up neither."

"Goody," my baby sister said. "Goody, goody!"

Dad didn't see it that way. The dealer had swapped them a Chevrolet six years older than the Oldsmobile. "Did the man pay Ralph any boot?"

Aunt Nica looked at him like he was dim-witted. "Cource not. Hit don't differ narry a bit what's writ on the thing. Don't you see this'en runs like a treddle machine. The Oat-see-mobile was sick."

137

Dad never brought up talk about cars to her again.

The very next month Aunt Nica got back right at supper time and looked more tired than before.

Dad had not went for her this time; someone had dropped her off without coming in. She came into the kitchen and sat down by Mama without saying one word.

She wouldn't eat a bite. I could tell, it worried Mama, put her hand on Aunt Nica's arm. "Are you sick?"

After a spell Aunt Nica reached for the coffee cup, took a long swallow, and looked at Mama. "You'ens ever been down to that Tenn-e-seee?"

"Why shore." Dad took a sip of coffee. "We got kinfolks there."

"Well, I ain't never been to no sech a place in all my born days."

"Pray tell, what happened?" Mama said.

"Ole Doker Tice, he took to preaching. Got called by a church down in that Tenn-e-seee."

"So? Lord, woman, it ain't far to Tennessee. You can throw a rock down there. We go there and back fore dinner."

"Nothin would do Ole Doker but us to follow him down that on Saturday, spend the night at his house, and hear him preach next mornin."

This time he didn't see the dirty look.

"Who's is we?" My oldest sister said.

I done and figured what was coming next.

"Why, Virgie Mae, Ralph and me. Who else could it be? Anyways, Doker was to lead the way."

"What did he preach on?" Mama said.

"Glory, we never heered him preach. When we got down thar to that Tenn-e-seee, I declare there was a beer jiant here and a beer jiant thar. People all out in street. . . ."

By now she was all out of breath, so Mama went and got her a fresh cup of coffee from the stove. Dad covered his mustache with his hand. "What's in God's world has a beer joint got to do with hearing this fellow preach?"

I felt Mama kick him on the leg, under the table.

"Well sir, hit's got a right smart to do with it. I told Ralph I could see to spy us out a way in the daylight, but couldn't see to spy out no way iff'en dark set in on us."

I could tell Dad wanted to come back with something, but he got up and poured fresh coffee in his cup. He don't want to be kicked no more, I guess.

"What happened then?" My younger sister said, before Dad could swallow.

"Well, I seed a beer jiant up ahead with three big log trucks parked in front and I told Ralph right then and thar, 'turn this thing around and head for Tater Town.'"

Dad snickered. Mama kicked. Missed him. Hit me.

"Didn't get to hear this Tice fellow preach?" Mama said.

"Lordy no. Doker, he hunted for us til way in the night. Then somebody told him they had seed us goin through the Mulberry Gap on our way to Tater Town."

Every since Aunt Nica came, she took up with Frank and Betty Bentley. They lived just across the creek, but they had to use another road to get to their place. Dad and Frank tore out the foot-log and made a good bridge so'es Aunt Nica and Betty could visit together.

The Bentleys raised tame rabbits in a hutch behind their house. Their pride and joy was a big buck that looked like a fluffy snow ball. "Pure white rabbits are scarce as hen's teeth." Aunt Nica told me over and over again. When the Bentleys were gone for any length of time, she took it on herself to tend their rabbits.

Aunt Nica was down by the creek on day making lye soap--the only kind she'd use to wash with. Me and my younger sister were helping.

"Why do you make soap?" My sister said.

140

"That store-bought soap is a waste of money and time. Hit's so weak, you cain't get narry a thing clean. Besides which, we need the lye to make hominy with."

"That store-bought soap might be pizen," my sister said. "Besides, I don't like hominy grits."

"You don't make a lick of sense," I said. "And anyway, Mama better not hear you talk like that. She'll wash your mouth out with soap, again."

"Yuck!"

We were working away, boiling the soap down until it suited Aunt Nica. I tried to keep the fire stoked up just right. My sister played in the fire with a stick; kept the coals raked out from under the iron wash-pot. It kept me busy putting them back.

Low and behold Ole Speck, our best tree dog, came across the bridge with the white rabbit in his mouth.

"Yoke him, and get that rabbit a'fore he kills it!" Aunt Nica said.

I caught the dog as he cleared the bridge and took the rabbit out of his mouth. It was cold and stiff. "It's dead as a doornail," I said,

"Besides," my sister said, "it's covered with old red mud. Yuck!"

"And what difference does that make?" I said. "He's stone cold dead."

I laid him by the wash pot. They looked him over and my sister picked him up. "He's stiff as a poker."

"Confound you, Speck." Aunt Nica hurried with her soap making. "After I finish bilin this soap, I'll tend to you!"

Ole Speck put his tail between his legs, like he does when we scolded him. My sister picked up a rock the size of a guinea egg.

"Don't you dare rock my dog!" I said.

"Lordy, lordy," Aunt Nica said, "what in this world will I tell Betty?"

"I don't have no idea."

"Confound you, Speck." My sister picked up the battlin stick Aunt Nica used to beat the clothes clean on a rock. "I'll beat your brains out."

"You'll not hit my dog."

Ole Speck must have heard enough; he headed for the house in a dead lope.

"Least we can do is clean the poor thing up." I said.

Aunt Nica turned to me. "Go over to Betty's and see if he kilt any more."

"What'll I say to them?"

"They ain't to home. Gone to visit their boy over on Clear Creek. Won't be back til late."

"I never liked them rabbits no-how." My sister said."

I slipped over to the Bentleys. The rabbits were all in their cages, nibbling on lettuce.

When I got back, they had cleaned the mud off the rabbit. With all the soap and water, I guess it was the right thing to do. It wasn't long before they had laid him on a rock to dry. He looked a right smart better.

"What you go'na tell Mrs. Bentley?" My sister said.

Aunt Nica thought for an awful long time. "Confound that dog," was all she said.

I knew Aunt Nica didn't care for Reek. Now she had it in for his favorite dog.

After the cakes of soap were set out to dry, Aunt Nica picked up a towel and fluffed the rabbit's fur up. Now we had to come up with what to do with him.

"Let's put his corkus back in the cage," my sister said.

"Confound you Speck," Aunt Nica said, when she saw Speck standing on the far bank.

"You want me to bury him?" I said.

"You skin him and make me something out of the pelt." My sister said.

That seemed to settle it. I picked up the rabbit and carried him back and laid him in the hutch.

We had just sat down to supper when we heard a commotion from over at the Bentley's. We quit eating and walked out on the porch. Betty yelled to the high heavens.

I looked at Aunt Nica. She looked ready to faint. While the others milled around I helped her set down in a chair.

"What's all the whooping about?" Dad said. "She's squawling loud enough to warp the gates of hell."

"They must be snake bit," Mama said.

Mama and Dad took off toward the Bentleys, in a trot. We followed along behind, not knowing what to do or say. Aunt Nica lagged behind; her face was white as a sheet. I had tried all day to come up with the right words to tell the Bentleys, but my sister would tell something else anyway.

Ole Speck didn't follow; he must know that when Dad finds out what took place he'll give him a whooping.

"Betty!" Dad said. "What on earth is the matter?"

Betty's face was all blotchy. "It skeered me half out of my skin. Day before yesterday, that old buck rabbit died and Frank buried him. Now he's back in his cage."

Another baby got born two months later. We were all tickled, even though Mama didn't have any free time now.

"Shaw, she's the spittin image of the last one." Reek said with a grin that reached from ear to ear.

"Well by thunder, I'll leave home when she's four." I said.

I worried that Aunt Nica was going back to Tater Town, now that the baby got born. If that was what she planned, she never let on.

"Your Dad and Nica gets along like two sore tail cats." Mama said, that spring, when she was on her feet again.

"You need to plant your taters on Good Friday," Aunt Nica said, to Dad the first week in April. "The signs are right."

"I plant my crops in the ground," Dad said, "not on the moon."

"Won't be big as marbles, neither."

I went outside to graze the cow on the young grass that had come up along the creek. Just as I figured, the potatoes were cut and ready to plant on Thursday before Good Friday.

Later that summer Aunt Nica brought a bowl of boiled cabbage to the table. "We need to make kraut tomorrow."

"The cabbage heads will be a lot bigger in a couple of weeks." Dad said.

"Yes," Aunt Nica said, "and the signs will be in the feet. The kraut will stink so bad you'll have to hold your nose with one hand and eat with the t'other."

Three days later we filled two twelve-gallon crocks with sauerkraut.

Mama and my sisters wear long dresses she makes from feed sacks. Some of the cloth is printed pretty but it's hard to fine enough sacks alike, to make anything bigger than a dress. The scraps they sew into quilts. Mama put a lot of stock in the fact that we all have clean clothes every day

At night Aunt Nica had my sisters doing what she called, "Woman's work." Folks came from all over to buy the quilts she and my sisters made. She wouldn't sell anything that one of my sisters wanted or would put in their trunks in the loft.

"Them girls got enough bed covers to last them, if they raise a passel of young'ens." Dad hit his head on the quilting frame that hung near the ceiling during the day and was lowered in the evening when they worked on it. "This contraption is always in the way."

"I don't want to quilt, no how." One of my sisters said after she stuck a needle in her hand again.

"You'ns were born tired and raised lazy, just like Reek." Aunt Nica said.

In time, folks had commenced moving in our country, seeking summer homes places. Aunt Nica didn't call them by name; she just said, "Them comers and goers."

Real-estate brokers swarmed like locusts--but acted like vultures-- as they chased the fast bucks that could be made off selling old home places.

Ed Riley died leaving no kinfolks. His place was called Hard Scrabble, but it was one of the finest hillside farms in these parts. The homestead was a decent house and barn set on sixty acres of cleared land.

From early spring until late fall, folks came asking about it. One hot evening in August, a big car drove up and a stranger came up to where Aunt Nica was busy sprinkling ashes on her roses.

"I've been looking at that run down farm down the road," he said. "I think they call it the Riley place. What kind of people live around here?"

"What kind of neighbors did you have where you come from?"

The man stuck his chest out, like a rooster. "They were a bunch of sorry good-for-nothings, who didn't work hard and try to help themselves. That's the reason I left--sorry people lived around there."

Aunt Nica hit at a weed with the hoe she always carried. "I'm a'feared you'll find the folks around here the same way."

"Well, I'm glad you told me." The man turned and walked back to his car, like he knew everything already. Didn't even bid a good evening or thank Aunt Nica.

Later that very evening, another man came to our door. He looked a lot like the first one. "I hate to bother you this near to dinner time, but I'm interested in the Riley Place."

"How so?" Aunt Nica wiped her hands on her apron.

"I'm well pleased with the place, but I wanted to meet and see what type of neighbors I'd have."

"What kind of neighbors did you have where you come from?"

"They're the reason I hate to leave, they're a great bunch--I know I'll miss them."

"I believe you'll find the folks around here to your liking."

The man thanked her and left. I didn't look to see what kind of car he drove, there is so many around now.

My little sister jumped straight up. "You told one of them men a story."

"No, child. The truth is, a neighborhood is what you make of it. I'm sure both them men will find it the way they want it to be."

That night at supper, Dad listened to one of my sister tell about the men, then held his coffee cup with both hands.   He always did that when something bothered him. "I'd sure love to have that place.   These kids will be needing a place to live some-day."

"How much they ax'in for hit." Aunt Nica said.

"Five thousand dollars." Dad said.   "It don't matter; we couldn't raise a hundred."

Mama had that hurting look on her face again.

"Ain't that much money in the whole wide world," my oldest sister said.

The look on Mama's face grew. The same one I saw when we first went to see the furniture. I still hate that look. She was about to cry as she tried to speak. "Let's forget about it."

"Is it worth the price?" Aunt Nica said.

I wish Aunt Nica would hush, before Mama's chin quivered.

"Oh, yes," Dad said. "Has a big tobacco allot-ment even."

"You ought to buy it then." Aunt Nica said.

"What with?" Dad said.

I wish they would hush. We are no better off now than when we first went to look at Aunt Nica's furniture. The blue mold had struck again and it had turned off dry after that. The tobacco plants were about half the size they ought to be. We had only got one good cutting of hay; the second cutting would be so thin and dry, Dad turned the stock in on it. Most time, the corn was nothing but nubbins the last four or five rows, up against the timber. This year it wasn't worth nothing all the way down to where the ground leveled off, right above the house.

"You could ask at the bank." Mama's chin quivered.

"Already did. They'll loan us the money all right; only thing is we cain't meet the payments. What with school coming on and all these mouths to feed. . . . . ."

Aunt Nica left the kitchen without saying a word. I hoped she's not mad at what Dad said. I wished she wouldn't go back to Tater Town.

I watched Mama's face. I hate that look. I hate the quivering. I wish I'd never heard of that old land.

A few minutes Aunt Nica came back with the Bible under her arm, just like she had when she came to live with us. Was she figuring on going home right now? She laid it down in front of Dad.

"It won't do any good to pray over it," he said, "I done that already too."

"I aim to do a heap more than pray over it." Aunt Nica opened the Bible.

Between every single page was money; Most hundreds, many fifties, but nothing less than a twenty.

"Lordy! Lordy! Lordy!" Mama said. "You've been keeping that money in this house. What if there is a fire?"

"Hit's the good book," Aunt Nica said. "Fire would burn the edges off the pages, but not back in the folds."

Dad swallowed hard. "How much is there?"

Aunt Nica pulled out bills and laid them in front of him. "Don't rightly know--ain't counted it in years."

"You may need the money." Mama said.

Aunt Nica grinned. "Pray tell, what in this world for? Besides, thar's other books."

When they'd counted out the five thousand, I looked at the book. They had took money from only a few pages and the Bible had over a thousand.

The happy look on Mama's face was the best ever. It stayed and stayed and stayed. I wish this day could last forever.

Aunt Nica was pleased to replace the money with pictures of my sisters and four leaf clovers they found.

After all was said and the deed made, they argued same as before. Aunt Nica never cut Dad any slack, and he never let up on her.

One thing has stuck in the day-book of my mind. From that day until this, Dad made it clear, the place would never be called Hard Scrabble or the Riley Place. He made sure nobody ever called it anything other than the Aunt Nica Place.

AZ STOKER ----- THE LONER

"There was another shooting in town last night," the feed store man, Mr. Ledbetter, said.

"What did they shoot up this time?" a farmer said, from back behind the stove. "They've blamed near took over the town."

"What shooting?" Dad said.

"If'en you-uns ain't heard," Mr. Ledbetter said, "it's been a spell since you've been in town."

Dad and I had come to town at first light. We made the feed store on the edge of town our first stop. To catch up on the farm news, Dad called it. Mama allowed it was gossip.

"We been grubbing on a new ground, and it being planting time, I guess it's been a couple of months," Dad said.

"Them hellions dang near ruint the town, shot up a bunch of stuff and stole everything that ain't nailed down," Mr. Ledbetter said. "Last night it was a streetlight, road signs, and one of the tires on the police car".

"What police car?" Dad said, "We don't have no police car. What about the sheriff?"

"He don't give a tinker's damn," the farmer said. "Says it's out of is jury-diction."

I moved close to Dad. I have never seen a police car. I wondered if it has a siren and a light on top.

"That bunch at the courthouse is all a kin," Mr. Ledbetter said, spitting tobacco juice across the counter and out the door. "Besides, they all live out of town a'ways, anyhow."

"Let me tell it straight." The farmer got off his nail keg. "The whole county bunch is laying out ever night down at the Poplar Lodge. They have a hootenanny thar ever night."

"Sheriff too?" Dad said.

"High Sheriff too." Mr. Ledbetter pulled at the sleeve garter on his right arm.

"What's folks to do?" Dad said.

"Well, I heard they went and hired Az Stoker for a town police," the farmer said. "Mr. Strubbs and Seth Vest made'um."

"Oh, they hired him all right," Mr. Ledbetter nodded. "Even bought an old Packard police car."

"Have to pay him an arm and a leg, I've heard," another farmer said. "Course they'll fire him the minute he gets things settled down. Then them thugs'll gang up and flog him before they run him out of town. They all'us do."

"Yesterday was his first day," Mr. Ledbetter said.

"I knew Az Stoker," Dad said, "when they built the dam over at Rimer's Ferry."

"A real hard knot," the farmer said. "He's the one that straightened out that hell-raisin bunch over in Sweetwater."

Our town is not wide, but it was plenty long. It sets on what us folks that live above town call War Woman Creek. In town they didn't like that name and couldn't make up their minds on what to call it. So they just call it the creek. Anyway, the town stretches out for maybe a half-mile up and down the thing. The only place in town where two roads run in the same way is where the main road forks and bends around the Courthouse Square.

The main part of town has some big fine houses that belonged to the timber bosses. The only other ones worth a hoot are the hotels and boarding houses where the work hands stay.

Dad winked and nodded toward the door. "Got to go pay some on my taxes." Paying taxes and getting nails are by-words Dad uses when he don't want to let on what's on his mind. We left the feed store and headed for town, I knew Dad was going to see this Az Stoker fellow.

He parked the truck and we headed for the courthouse. He took a delight in listening when they had court, and they were having it today.

"Will they fire that fellow once he does a good job here?" I said.

"They may let him go," Dad said. "They've been know to."

There was no one on the steps or in the hallway, so we went straight back to the courtroom. Dad slid across a bench half way back in the room. "There's the ones, that took part in the shooting. The ones we were talking about."

"Them fellows don't look none too good all wrapped up in all the white bandages," I said "And they sure didn't waste no time getting around to tryin'em."

"A bond hearing," Dad said.

"What's a bond hearing?" I asked, but got no answer.

The courtroom held fifteen double rows of benches that looked like they came from a big church somewhere. You could hear well if nobody was walking on pine floor. It squeaked like a little kid playing with a fiddle.

"Tell us what happened after they shot out your tire," the judge said to a man setting in the witness chair.

"Light rain was fallin last night as I rounded the Courthouse Square," said the man with a star on is shirt and a flat brimmed hat in his left hand.

"That's Az Stoker," Dad said as he leaned back. "He ain't aged much."

Az Stoker was not big, as mountain men go. He was a little under six feet tall and I guess he weighed one seventy or about. I reckon that is why I noticed his hands right off. They hung from arms too long for his body, like hams of meat. His coal black eyes set way back in his face. The kind of eyes that can stare a hole plumb through a body.

"Boom!" Az Stoker said. "One of the streetlight globes busted, showered the car with glass. The rain must have got in the thing, I thinks to myself."

"Them globes is big as a number-five washtub," A man in the crowd said.

"Boom!" Az said, "I heered it again. This time I saw a streak of white fire from a gun barrel. The car, it swerved to the right, barely missin a big oak tree in Mrs. Johnson's yard."

"What did you do then?" the judge fellow said.

"Why, I turned off the car lights and rolled out the far side. I seen where a shotgun blast had tore the tire blamed near in threads."

Now there was not even a whisper in the courtroom. Dad moved closer to the edge of his seat. So did most of the other folks.

157

"Go on," the judge said.

"With my left hand, I felt under the seat for my old sawed-off shotgun and pulled it out by the stock. Hit was loaded; I was ready fur'um."

Now, nobody in the courtroom moved, and for a long time neither Az nor the judge spoke.

"It's like I told you, your honor," Az said. "I checked my shotgun."

"A twelve-gauge," the judge said, "that's what you carry? Right?"

"Yeah."

"Go on."

"I seen a man run through Miss Mandy Forest's yard, wavin a gun. He shot up towards where I wuz."

"Did he hit anything?"

"Don't rightly know, cause, I cut drive."

"You mean you shot at him?"

Az Stoker nodded.

"Did you hit him?" the judge said.

"I reckon. He cut a flip."

"Then what happened?"

"Another'n run down the alley-way. He pointed a gun and shot, heather and yon. I let go the other barrel. The rifle he was a carryin went sailin through the air end over end."

"Is that the only shots you fired?"

"Yes, Your Honor. All I could see after that was rear ends and elbows as they scattered."

Everybody laughed.

"Proceed," the judge said, when the noise died down.

"I carried the two that were down, over to Doc Prichard's. Your honor, these boys ought to be more keerful. Why, iff'en it wasn't for them heavy duck-back coats they wuz a wearin--why, they'd be laid out a corpse."

His voice was calm, though a little high-pitched. Anyone could tell by the words he used that he was from way back up in the mountains, somewhere. When he got to his feet, I saw a pistol strapped on his side, which reached almost to his knees. An eight-inch blackjack stuck out of his back pocket.

We left the courtroom and made our way out to the porch. Dad stopped just outside the door and leaned back up against the wall. I stood beside him while I looked to see if the police car was in sight.

"This town's never had no two-bit cop before," said a county big-shot, the was the son of one of the timber buyers; he pranced like a stud horse. "That no-good son-of-a-bitch shot my sister's boy last night."

People gathered fast to listen to him. He was well over six-foot and had to weigh some over two-fifty, or better. "I'll show that country cop a thing or two. . ."

The more he rambled on, the bigger the crowd got. The womenfolk and the more timid souls went and stood in the street. Dad and I stood against a wall beside the courthouse doors. It looked as if this big fellow was going to beat up Az Stoker. Or at least dress him down in front of the crowd.

I didn't have time to be scared, for out of the corner of my eye, I saw Az Stoker. I hoped Dad would warn him somehow. It was too late, Az walked down the hallway, not twenty feet away; coming straight for the door.

The big-shot stepped right out in front of Az and stuck a finger in his face. "You son-of-a-bitch. I'll have your balls!"

I never saw it coming, it happened so fast. Az's fist came from somewhere down near his knees and lifted the big-shot clear off the ground. For a thought the man froze in mid-air. His eyes rolled back as if he'd done went and died.

He hit the marble floor with a thud. Az put his right hand under the man's arm and drug him over against the wall. He dusted off the man's hat, placed it on the fellow's head, and started down the steps with Dad.

"How've you been?" Az said, to Dad as they walked along.

"Two lessons I think the town learned today," Dad said, back to the feed store. "First, if you try to hurt him you're apt to get yourself killed. The other is, if you call him a S.O.B, he'll bust your brains out with his fist."

About half way home, I remembered the police car again. "I'll have to look at it another time. I hope they don't fire Az Stoker."

The town was quite that winter and until mid-July. Talk at the feed store turned to other things. Lots of it about the war.

Then two Badcock brothers came to town having just built part of a hitch in the marines.

Luther married Simon Hornsbuckle's girl, Nell, and moved into the old Walt Jarrett place. Gosnell, the oldest and biggest, seemed to want to be the town bully.

One Saturday night the Sanders brothers and some of us boys passed through town. We had been camping out and fishing down on the Hiawassee for a week. A little while after dark we stopped in town to show off our fish.

Gosnell and a bunch of drunks had landed in at the local gas station. White liquor flowed like spring water. Gosnell told big war stories and got meaner by the minute. He sat in Mr. Cecil Long's chair with his feet on top of the desk.

"That there is real hell-roarin bunch," Pearley Sanders said, as he pulled the truck behind the building where we could hear and see what was going on without being noticed. After a week of laying out, even the older Sanders boys did not want to get into any fuss.

Mr. Long, who was known to drink a little too much now and then, had long since passed out in the grease rack.

In and around the place there must have been twenty-five or thirty men. I saw the old police car pass and Az look over the crowd. He paid no mind, as if he wanted to let them have what fun they could.

"Suey!" Gosnell said, the next time Az passed.

Some others commenced yelling, "Suey! Suey!"

Az rode by a few more times. I guess he hoped they'd drink up what they had, and go home. Close to midnight they got so loud the neighbors woke up and lit their lamps, trimmed the wicks to make them give off as much lights as they would. I knew Az wouldn't stand for all this commotion, long.

"Suey!" someone yelled the next time Az passed.

"SUEY!" Gosnell yelled so loud, I know they heard it all over town. The plate glass in the station windows shook from all the noise they made.

"Suey. Suey! Suey!"

Az turned his car around and drove slowly back toward the station. I figured he was going to stop, if the racket didn't quieten down.

"Suey, Suey! SUEY!" several whooped.

162

Ever so slow, Az drove the old Packard through the crowd and parked beside the door. He got out and walked through the men. He never said a word until he was in the station.

"Take your feet off Mr. Long's desk. . . .Now."

"You go to hell!" Gosnell said.

Az slapped Gosnell's feet so hard the marine went around and around in the swivel chair, then landed on his back by the counter. The look on Az's face froze everybody in their place. The only sound was a cricket, chirping, on the window ledge.

"I heard somebody a callin his hog," Az said. "Who was it?"

No one made a sound or moved an eye lid.

"Where's that hog caller now?" Az said. His black eyes darted from one of the men to another.

The men backed up against the wall, like they were holding it up. Gosnell staggered to his feet.

"Where's that hog caller now?" Az pointed his finger in Gosnell's face. "Boy, was it you that lost his hog? I believe it was."

He was right in the face of Gosnell, who had made it to his feet and was steadying himself on the desk with both hands. I saw the veins stick out on Az's face. Gosnell saw it too.

"Call your hog, boy."

"Suey," Gosnell said, in a voice I barely could make out.

"Call your hog like you mean it," Az said. "A while back, I heard you all over town."

"Suey!" Gosnell said, a little louder.

"Again."

"Suey, Suey! SUEY!"

Az turned away. Ol Gosnell's face trembled--he looked, about to cry.

"You call you a hog," Az said to Albert Smith, who weighed better than two hundred and fifty pounds and stood well over six feet.

"Hit wern't me." Albert said. "Suey . . ."

Az went through the crowd, made half of them call. "Suey." Most had their eyes fixed on their feet. I was sure glad to be out back in the dark.

"Con-sarn it," Az said, "I don't hear a good hog caller amongst you."

Ten minutes after he left; the crowd was gone. We high-tailed it home without ever showing off our fish.

"I sure don't want to show that mean old bastard my catfish," Earl Sanders said, "he might think it was a hog-sucker and hang me."

I looked for them to band together and get the tar bucket after Az. I reckon they were put out with themselves after he called their bluff. Anyhow, I never heard it talked about again.

From then on there was not a soul over the age of ten brave enough, or dumb enough, to mock him. Later it came to me that I had been within twenty feet of the police car and couldn't recall anything, but it was black. All cars were.

"Them county officials is keeping the road hot, running up and down the coves and branches," Dad said, one day while we were at Miller's Mill, talking to Mr. Calhoun and buying school britches. "They're trying to get rid of Az claiming, the town pays him way more than the High Sheriff gets."

"We hired him so we could have peace and quiet," Mr. Calhoun said. "We got it. If we was to let him go, the peace and quiet'll go with him. And I'm the mayor."

Dad brushed his hat band with his hand. "They claim they'll get you un-elected."

Election talk made some folks look like the blight got their corn crop. I couldn't make no sense out of any of it. Dad talked about some of it to me. "Some of the big-shots in town are apt to do anything to keep Mayor Calhoun from being re-elected. They figure that's the only way they'll be able to get rid of Az, since Mr. Calhoun won't fire him. They've already made their brags as to how they'll run ole Az out of the county on a rail, time the election is over."

"Don't everybody have a say about who the mayor is?" I said. "I hope they don't send...off Az Stoker."

165

"Commonly, they do, but you cain't never tell what some people'll do to get their way."

About the only thing I could make out of all of it was that it carried a lot of weight with some folks like Dad, for Az to stay. There were others who tried about anything they could figure out to see him leave. "It won't be long now. I hope Az don't have to go."

Dad twisted the corner of his mustache with his fingers. "Guess we cain't do nothing; cept wait and see."

"Ol Judge Seabolt is a courting Miss Maybelle Fink on the weekends," Dad said one night, while we sat around the kitchen table. "I hear tell they've seen him over there all hours of the night."

"In the summer he gathers things from his garden and she cans them for him," Mama said. "He cuts her winters wood."

It was plain to me Mama liked Miss Maybelle Fink or Judge Seabolt. If Mama liked you, you could do no wrong. If not, you couldn't do much of anything right.

"The other Saturday morning," Dad went right on, "the judge headed over to her place, in a hurry. Just as he drove past the old Indian School, down on Sandy Mush, he passed Az Stoker."

"So?" Mama said.

"Az motioned for him to pull over. 'Say, judge,' says Az. 'Didn't you see the ten-mile-an-hour sign, back there a ways?' The judge, he tore into Az. 'Don't be a fool, that old school's been closed for ten years. Besides it's the middle of July, all the schools are closed.'"

"Az fired back. 'Con-sarn it judge, if'en they want you to go faster they'll take the plagued sign down.'"

Dad licked his upper lip like he always does when he gets Mama's goat. Her face turned red, she got up and started washing the supper dishes, like she was in hurry to get to bed.

Judge Seabolt paid the $3.50 fine, we heard down at the feed store Saturday. The next week, we saw the state highway workers take the sign down.

Things settled down here in the high country. We didn't hear Az Stoker's name spoke until one day three months later, when Dad really needed to go to town.

". . . . Well, Az can always help them catch Billy Brody," Mr. Ledbetter said to a farmer, as we walked in the feed store, the third Friday in November.

"He's gone again," a farmer said, when Dad asked what they were talking about. "That boy won't stay in their chain gang. Hit's as simple as that."

"Two of them prison guards were in here day a'for yesterday, buyin feed for their dogs," Mr. Ledbetter said.

"Why were they not out they chasing after him?" Dad said.

"I'll tell it straight." The farmer said. "No cold-nose bloodhound can track that Indian boy,"

"The guards said it wern't no use," Mr. Ledbetter said. "That boy can travel for miles, without touching the ground, by swingin on grape-vines and ridin down saplings."

"I hear tell he traveled the river one winter and the guards nearly froze their asses off trying to track him," the farmer said.

"What was he doing time for?" Dad said.

"We talked about that yesterday. No one can rightly recollect what the original charge was," Mr. Ledbetter said, "less it was for killing old man Tillie's mule: eight year ago."

"Any others escape with him?" Dad said.

"No, the other hundred or so are still clearin a right of way up on Greasy Spoon Creek."

As we had done often since Az came, Dad and I went to the courthouse. We stopped by to see if they were having court, Judge Seabolt called a bunch of lawmen up before him. "I want that boy brought before this court!" The judge said. "The Governor wants to know why you cain't keep him locked up."

"That's about as close as I've ever heard the judge come to ordering a bench warrant," a lawman said, as they walked by us.

"We'd better go see Az Stoker," the other one said.

"What's a bench warrant?" I said to Dad.

He hasn't answered me yet.

The old Brody place lay across one ridge from the cove, less than two miles away. I slipped off over there every once in a while to see Mrs. Brody. To tell the truth, mainly, I went for the fudge candy she kept in her dresser drawer. In the back of my mind, I hoped to see if Billy was there.

Next morning as I walked down through her garden, I saw Az Stoker's car winding its way up toward the house. It was all covered with mud from the drive up Dry Bed Road. Someone came out the side door of the house so fast I blinked, afraid to trust my eyes. He ran like a spooked deer to a big hemlock tree above the spring.

I hunkered down in the tool shed where I could see what went on. Mrs. Brody sat rocking on the porch, stringing green beans on a thread.

Az walked up and put his foot on the big rock they used for a step. "My name's Az Stoker."

"I knowed who you aire," Mrs. Brody said.

"Is Billy hereabouts?"

"Not in the house, he ain't."

For just a minute, Az's black eyes darted all around. I held my breath afraid he would see me move and shoot or something. I didn't figure he saw who ever it was that hid behind the tree, him driving the car around the big boulders and all.

Before I could bat my eyes, Az pulled the big long pistol and fired three shots into the hemlock. Tree bark rained all over the hillside. Far away as I was, the sound hurt my ears--not like no pistol I'd ever heard; more like a cannon.

"Come out and show yourself, Billy Brody." Az held the big gun with both hands. It put me in mind of a smoking hoe handle.

Billy came out from behind the tree. He walked right to the porch, where Mrs. Brody rocked, and strung her beans. She never let on like she heard or seen a thing.

"Can I step up here and take off these boots?" Billy said. "Their Granny's. She wears'em cepting if she a going to meetin."

Az nodded, and in less than a minute, he had loaded Billy in the old Packard and they were out of sight, down the road. Mrs. Brody kept on rocking and stringing her beans.

I slipped back up through the garden. I forgot the candy. I forgot about looking at the police car.

"They put Billy in the new solitary confinement unit," a guard told Mr. Ledbetter, while we sat on a sack of shelled corn over in a corner of the feed store, a few weeks later.

"What's that like?" Mr. Ledbetter said.

"It's a brand new building made out of cement blocks. It ain't got any windows. To get in you have to go through two thick steel doors, with different keys."

"Must be something to see."

"Oh, I'd say it is. Every twenty minutes a guard goes through the first door and looks in at the prisoner."

"What's inside?"

"That's the beauty of the place. All its got is a steel slab hung on chains for a bed. And a toilet built floor-level."

"I've never heard of such!" A farmer said.

"Besides," the guard said, "the inmates don't have nothing on cept their undershorts. I tell you, it's escape-proof."

"How's it het?" The farmer said.

"A coal stove in the room between the doors. The inmates cain't get near it."

Two weeks later the guard came back for more dog food. Dad and I sat in the back of the feed store, hid out from the thunderstorm that had hung around here in the mountains for three days.

171

"How's Billy a doin?" Mr. Ledbetter said.

"Hell fire, he's gone," the guard said.

"Looks like Billy don't know what escape-proof means," Dad whispered.

Mr. Ledbetter snickered. "Well I'll be. How in the world? For the life of me, I don't see.... "

"They figured he used the acid in his urine to dissolve the mortar in the joints," the guard said. "Stuffed toilet paper back in place of the mortar so we couldn't tell it was gone."

"Last Thursday night, he kicked a hole in the wall and walked away."

"I do declare . . . " Mr. Ledbetter laughed.

About a month later Dad and I stopped at Cecil Long's station, trying to put a boot in one of our truck tires, when the mail carrier stopped by. He was all in a lather. "Word came over the wire that two desperate felons jumped the train as it pulled up out of the Nantahala Gorge."

"We've done and heard," Cecil Long said, "they're wanted for murder in Tennessee."

"White slavery too," Verg, his hired hand, said.

"What in the world were they doing in these parts?" Dad said.

"I hear tell the law captured them in South Carolina and was taking them to Knoxville." Cecil, wiped his face with his greasy shirttail. "It ain't no rumor; the law done told folks to lock their doors."

"Big city like that's full of cut-throats," Verg said. "I know. I've been thar."

Our valley lay in the path the criminals would take if they knew anything about traveling in the mountains, or followed the river. Folks bolted their doors for the first time in years.

Four days later, the rolling store man told us the law had them locked up. The next morning Dad wanted to go to town. Claimed he had to have some number 16-penny nails, to fix the corn crib. We hadn't been to town in weeks and the work here was caught up. Never fooled Mama. She just shook her head and grinned. Two hours later Dad and I walked up the courthouse steps.

A bunch of people stood at the back of the courtroom; had Az Stoker backed into the corner. They fired questions like a corn sheller spits out corn.

"Why did you. . . ."

"Wern't you afraid?"

"Where'd you catch'um?" a man said, louder than the others.

"Mossy Rock Gap." Az said

"I know where that is," another man, pointed out the window. "Hit's the lowest gap you can see off yonder, fuderest to the west."

A few people went over to the windows and pointed to the high mountains that stood between us and the Little Tennessee River. I looked at the haze-covered mountain tops, but couldn't see the gap.

"Were you by yourself?" A man asked Az.

"Wern't no use in taking a bunch. There's only two of'um."

"How'd you know they would come that way?" a man from the newspaper said. "Or what time they'd be there?"

"I knowed they'd be travelin the old toll road or else the T.V.A. power line," Az said. "And both go through that gap."

"So how'd you know when?"

"I just figured how long it'd take a body to get there, a travelin at night, on foot."

I saw Az wanted to leave, but the people kept him backed in the corner. It seems they all yearned to learn more and there were lots here; it being after crop laying-by time.

"When did you go out there?" someone asked.

"Day-a-fore-yesterday," Az said. "Takes three hours to drive it. I got thar about dusky dark."

"The power line crosses the road at the gap," a man said.

Again Az tried to leave, but this time a woman stopped him. "Come on, tell us more."

"I drove past the gap and parked the car," Az said. "I ate a bite of supper. Then, I crawled up on the road bank and waited."

"Was it dark by then?"

"Yes ma'am. It were by the time I heard them a comin. They walked right up next to my car, then froze in their tracks."

"Go on," the woman said. "Please tell us what they did then."

"One of them fellows said, 'Hell, there sets their car. They're waiting on us!' Then they took off runnin back down the road."

"Did you chase'um?" a man said.

"No. I counted their steps, and after they stopped, I slipped out the road the same number, quiet as I could; walked on the high side of the road."

"Did they give you a tussle?" a gray-bearded man said.

"Not a bit. I flipped on my battery torch light; they lay hunkered down under the road bed."

"Did they say anything?" the woman said.

"They axed me if I had any water. Said they hadn't had a drink since they started up the mountain. I took'um to a spring just under the mountain top."

"Wern't you afraid they'd try to kill you?" the paper man said.

"They did whisper somethin about the old man being alone, while they laid there drinkin."

"So how did you haul them in, by yourself?"

"They started to climb in the back seat. It made me a mite mad that they thunk me that dumb."

Az started to leave again, this time he seemed more set on it.

"Please go on," the woman said. "Don't leave us hanging."

"I told them fellows to get in the front seat. Took my gun out and put it in my left coat pocket. Told them if they were a lookin for trouble, we'd have it out right then and thar. 'What's more,' I said to'um, 'if you reach for me or the wheel, I tend to kill you both.'"

"Did they say anything on the way back?"

"Slept, they did, till we got maybe a mile from town and they said, mister, 'we ain't had nothin to eat since we baled off the train.'"

"You didn't feed them?" The woman stepped right in front of Az. "Did you?"

"Yes ma' am, I did. I stopped at the bus station and told Miss Bessy to fix'um ever bite they could eat; I'd pay the bill. Hit ain't right for people to go hongry."

With this Az pushed his way through the crowd and hurried out through the crowd.

His cold black eyes hit me like a hammer. He stopped and patted my head with his huge right hand. "You're apt to get snake bit hiding in them old sheds."

One Saturday I was playing marbles down in front of the Baker Hotel, waiting for the picture show to open. A game went on there almost all the time because the ground was blue clay and as hard as slate. That day we had only three players and seven marbles between us. Six were chipped and didn't roll straight. I kept the three flint marbles Uncle Thee made me in my pocket; there's no way would I take a chance on cracking one of my rollie-holie marbles to win a blamed glass one.

"Did you hear what happened week a fore last?" Silas Rhodes, the town loafer and part-time jailer, said, to some other men who sat rocking on the porch. I quit the marble game and leaned on the step rail, to listen.

Silas was a man in his late fifties, who hung around town day and night. He lived with his mother down on the river behind town. She made their living raising fish bait.

I recall how the talk around our kitchen table had gone a few weeks back. "Silas got a tongue like a bell clapper." Dad said. "And his mouth ain't no prayer book, but he don't lie . . . .Much."

"Shaw." Reek followed with, "And good fisher a site."

"He's got a saint for a mother." Mama added.

I moved up to where I could hear better. I leaned against the picket wall under the porch.

A voice that came from back on the porch, out of my sight, started in. "No. What happened?"

"Well, by dang," Silas said, "I'll tell you. Hit was early last Thursday, a-week-a-go, Az, he caught two young roughens a stealin clothes off Miss Earl's clothes line."

"Did?" A second voice said.

"That's over at her boarding house? Right." The first voice said.

"The same," Silas said. "They wuz a cussin and raisin hell, when Az drug them into the jail."

"Like how?" the man said. "What wuz it they said or done?"

Silas stuck his chest out, as he went on with his story. "They told me. 'We've been traveling around for a year and nobody's laid a hand on us till now,' and all sech as that. They called Az pert-near every vile word you ever heerd. In the morning, they shook the bars on their cell and threw the chair at the window. Ever time a pretty girl walked by, they took all kind of fits, hollering and mocking. They raised hell all the blessed day long. If I hadn't been so used to staying in that thar old jail, I'd been scared. . . even."

"Did?" the second voice said.

"Sounds like a bunch of hellions all right," another voice said. "What went with them after that?"

"That night, it came down over the wire from Alabama," Silas said. "Seems like there was a string of warrants on them fellows, long as a man's leg."

"Did?" the second voice said.

"You don't say?" The first voice said.

"'We'll need to send you boys back to fess up,' Judge Seabolt said, when they went before him."

"Did?" the second voice said.

"Then they told the judge, 'Hell fire, we ain't about to sign no papers to go back to Alabama.'"

"Did?" the second voice said.

"And that ain't all neither," Silas said. "One of them fellers said to the judge, 'We're better off in this hick jail than in some Alabama prison. You hill-billies will just have to feed us this winter. Get a big coffee pot.'"

"Did?" the second voice said.

"I'll bet that made the old bastard mad," the first voice said.

"Hit did for a fact." Silas said. "Judge Seabolt stormed right down the hall and got on the telephone."

"Did?" The second voice said.

"The judge told Az, and me, not ten minutes later, 'They'll be here from Alabama by dark tonight; sendin a car.'"

"They must'a wanted them two powerful bad." The first voice said.

179

"For a fact, they did. Them Alabama law pleaded with them boys, but they wouldn't budge."

"Did?" the second voice said.

"Do they haf'ta sign?" The first voice said.

"No, and it takes months or even years for the Governors to get around to workin extradition out amongst themselves iff'en it comes down to it."

"Do?" the second voice said.

"Cost a bunch to feed and watch them for all that time," the first voice said.

"That's a fact. Az told them Alabama law to go over to the boardin house and wait."

"Did?" the second voice said.

"That was that, huh?" The first voice said.

"Naw. The next mornin, at four o'clock, Az raked a metal tray across the bars. 'What the hell?' one of the prisoners said."

"Az handed them two cold fried egg sandwiches. 'Breakfast.'"

"Did?" The second voice said.

"I recollect they feed good at the jail." Another man said.

"Do."

Then they all snickered.

"The fact is, generally they do. Well, them boys settled in and never heshed, laughed and yelled at every girl that passed on the street."

"Did?" The second voice said.

"Around mid-day the boys commenced askin, 'What's for lunch?'" Silas wasn't through. "'We call it dinner around here. Az, told'um'"

"Shore'a nuff?" The first voice said.

"Did?" The second voice added.

"'Well, what's for dinner?' One axed. "'We don't serve dinner.'" Az said.

That night around nine Az handed them two more cold egg sandwiches. "'Here's supper.'"

I heard only laughter coming from the porch now.

"The next mornin," Silas said, "Az done the same thing and by mid-day the men signed the papers and wuz on their way to Alabama."

"Did."

One morning, near election time, we came across a DeSoto touring car parked beside the bridge on the south side of town. The windshield and side windows were broken into smithereens. Dad didn't stop at the feed store; he drove straight to the courthouse. He didn't even make a joke about nails or taxes.

This time we had to wait an hour and a half before court took up. It was a worry to Dad that nobody there seemed to know anything about the car.

At nine-thirty they brought two men over from the jail. They could walk all right, but they looked pretty bad.

"That big'un looks like his head's been through a sausage grinder," Dad said.

"What happened last night?" Judge Seabolt said.

"Hit's like this here, Judge," Az said. "Late last night, I was settin out by the old Union Oil station on the north end of town."

"Go on. Then what?"

"This car come by, hit was mortally-a-flyin."

"Did you stop them?"

"Yes sir, I got the thing stopped on the other side of town. I asked'um if they didn't see our little speed limit sign back thar a-ways."

"What did they say to that?"

"The one that wern't drivin, he said, 'We didn't even see your hick town.'"

The veins in judge's forehead stood out. "Go on."

"Then I asked to see their papers on the car," Az said.

"They have any?"

"The driver reached for his back pocket, but the other one said, 'Don't show him a God d. . .' Well, judge, he used a bunch of vile words."

"Then what?"

"I went back to my car and got the ball bat. Come back and reached for the off-side door, but he locked it. He called me some more names."

"What names?"

"You know, the one about my mother."

"Oh, all-right, go on--did they try to run?"

"That's the part I'm a comin to. The big feller told the other to get the hell out of Hicksville."

"How did you stop them?"

"Broke the windshield with the first swing; next lick got the side glass. I couldn't get a good lick through the little side glass, but I poked him a plenty."

"I can see that. Then you took them to jail? Tell the court, how the deputy got hurt."

"That's the way it was. The big'un cussed and kicked the inside of my car all the way to the jail. He kept on a saying, 'We're mean where we come from.' He all but tore the door off."

"What about the deputy? How'd he get hurt?"

"When we got to the jail, I jerked the big-mouth out and kicked the door closed. I took the cuff of my hand slapped him a winding."

"I can see that. And the deputy? What about him?"

"I told the loud-mouth to hit that jail door as fast as he could. The deputy was sleepin in the jail and heard the commotion. Big-mouth tore out up the steps on all fours. He blamed near tore his fingernails off."

"It's plain you didn't molly-coddle him, but that still don't explain to the court how the deputy got knocked flat."

"I'm a comin to that. The deputy was standin on one leg, puttin on his britches; the big fellow come tearin through the door. He run square over the deputy."

The courtroom burst into laughter. It lasted so long the judge had to call a recess.

"Them big-city fellers sure was polite when they paid their fine," the clerk said, as we walked by.

"Az Stoker wants you to visit with him soon," the mailman told Dad the next year, right after the tobacco crop was hung up to dry.

We hadn't heard nothing of Az since the election, almost six months ago. Mr. Calhoun beat out that same fellow that Az hit at the courthouse; the one some of the town big-shots had tried to buy into the mayor's job.

"Go get Reek," Dad said to me, a few minutes after the mailman went down the cove.

"What'll I tell him you need him for?"

"Tell him we need to see a man about a dog."

I knew there was something up that Dad didn't want to talk about.

We'd not been to town in quite a spell, so Dad didn't waste no time; we left as soon as the evening feeding was done. Dad almost forget to turn the cow back into the pasture.

I didn't know where Az lived, but Dad drove straight into the yard of a little frame house on the north edge of town.

Az was sitting on the porch, whittling on a block of cedar, the shavings piling up in an old hat box at his feet.

"Howdy," Dad said. "How you doing?"

"Tolerable." Az came straight to the point. "Thar's a bunch makin rot-gut-licker up in Drovers Laurel. The revenuers claim they've hunted all over hell and half of Georgia for the still-house."

"It ain't no wonder," Dad said. "The place is hell on earth; folks been making pop-skull up there for a time and a time . . . none fit to drink."

I knew then why Dad wanted to bring Reek. He'd be a great help if you were trying to find anything in these mountains. Nobody knows the mountains like Reek does.

"Hit ain't no pop-skull this time," Az said. "Pizen. Done kilt a bunch of folks down in Nashville, it has. As well as three of the Miller boys over on Skeener."

"Shaw. Shaw," Reek said. "Must be a makin it with a truck radiator for a condenser; do it ever time."

"No. More likely they're usin acid pouring acid to make it have a higher proof." Az had a worried look on his face as he picked up his chair and walked into the house.

Now I got my chance to look the police car over good. It had a red light on top and it was a big thing, but the inside was worn to a frazzle, worse than our old truck. Two quilts and an old army coat covered the seat springs. Big holes in the floorboard were stuffed with toe sacks.

In a few minutes I followed them into the house. There was no furniture except the chair Az carried and one by the fire. Three blocks of red cedar lay on the mantle beside an old picture of a young woman. My sisters had more furnishings in their play house down by the barn.

While they talked low, I looked through the door into the kitchen. There were no cabinets or pot-hooks; just a table not over two foot square in the center of the room. On it sat one cup--one drinking glass-one fork-one spoon. A tin coffee pot and one frying pan rested on the stove.

Over my right shoulder I saw into the only other room. It held just an iron bedstead. On one of the bed posts hung a cross-cut saw blade, bent into a circle. I stepped into the room and slid it of the bedpost. The saw teeth had been filed off. It was easy to tell by the way it was curved and the small eye-hooks on the ends, it was something Az wore

around his chest. Even in the dim light I saw where
at least twice it had been hit by bullets; one a rifle
and the other a shotgun, both in the back.

We left a little after dark. I didn't ask Dad
what they had figured out about the still. The only
mention of Az was what Reek said. "Shaw that
place wuz as empty as last years's bird nests."

My mind kept going back to the old picture of
the young woman. After I got in bed I kept thinking
of one word that told the most about Az Stoker.

-----------Loner------

RUN AWAY SHAY - BREAKING TRACTION

"Did you ask that timber boss about me a job?"
I said to Dad and Reek when they come down from
the gap.

"I've told you fifty times, logging out-fits won't
hire nobody under fourteen," Dad said. "You're
barely eleven and don't look more'n eight."

"Tell'um I'm fourteen," I said. "I got to get me
enough money to buy a pair of them A A Cutter
boots before winter."

"Shaw," Reek said as he spit snuff between his
black logging boots. "You ain't big as a bar of soap
after a week's washin."

"That may be. But I got to figure me out some
way to come up with a pair of them boots."

Dad and Reek hurried off down the trail, like
they had to put out a fire. They didn't want to hear
no more, I reckon.

"Cain't ever get me sixty dollars hoeing corn
for Seth Vest for twenty-five cents a day!" I said as
they rounded the first bend ahead of me.

I went back in the house where my sisters were stringing beans. "Dad and Reek just told me I ain't tall enough to get no job."

"Hang by your hands from that apple tree limb." My oldest sister pointed toward the spring. "It'll make you taller, works every time." It was at least the tenth time she had said that this week.

"You wouldn't know a hawk from a handsaw!" I spit back.

I hung there all summer. The only difference between now and then, I can hang there a lot longer now. If I've stretched out one bit, it wern't enough for me to tell.

"Got you a job," Dad said one evening while he and Reek sat on the front porch, jawing.

"Shaw yes--you be the swamper. We surely do need us a swamper."

"What do a swamper do? I thought I knew about all the jobs in a logging camp, but I ain't never heard tell of a swamper."

"Shaw, he cleans the cook car and cuts the stove wood and all sech as that." Reek said. "You be the lobby hog, too."

"What's a lobby hog?"

"He cleans the bunk cars."

"Hot dang; now I got two jobs!"

"I mean to take you, but let me talk to your mother first." Dad said. "She'll bring up your Grandpa, again. And tell about how his sides were all scarred up from the ice floating down the river, back when they done log drives on the French Broad River."

This didn't sound good. Still, I've got to get them boots. I'd do about anything for them boots; done and looked at them at the Commissary, almost rubbed the black off, feeling of them. Anyway, if she let me go, by the time school started I'd have enough money to buy them. Might even take them to town and have hob nails put in the soles, like Reek's. I'd have to be quiet about this.

"Shaw," Reek said, every time he took off his boots to come in our house. "I take'um off to keep from a wearin out the hobs on the hard floor."

I knew it had to do with the morning Mama gave him mortal hell when he walked into the kitchen with his bob nail boots on. "Bleach this floor ever week with lye soap and ashes to keep it white. Sure don't mean to have it full of nail holes."

From then on Reek got earnest about wearing out his hob nails. I would do the same, I decided that night, as I lay in the loft thinking about them boots.

Come Sunday, Mama packed me up some things, along with Dad's. She sat them on the porch; never said one word about me going off to work.

The log train went back up in the mountains Sunday evening. Every house on some of the creeks sold whiskey and if the men walked; they'ed be drunk as a skunk. Some wouldn't show up till late in the week or not at all. The only liquor you could have in a logging camp was what you had already drunk, before you got there. The H. D. Lanier Lumber Company was willing to feed loggers one more night in order to have them sober Monday morning.

Everybody signed on to stay two weeks. "Shaw," Reek said. "If we had to stay any longer a body be dead, any shorter and we wouldn't make enough to keep us in snuff."

Dad and I stood down by the spring, until Reek came down the cove. I felt big as I walked with him and Dad over the ridge toward the big river. I would be getting me a paycheck. Maybe have enough to buy Mama something for letting me go out to work.

The logging camp was way up on the Eagle Fork of the Nantahala River, just below Standing Indian Bald. No one lived within fifty miles of the place. We had been there hunting and it took two weeks to tramp in and out. Living off rainbow trout and gray squirrels, we all lost weight.   It made Mama mad as fire.

"What if the train don't stop for us?" I asked Reek. "What if we don't hear it coming?"

"Shaw, shaw. Don't you fret and fume."

We walked up the track to where the trestle crossed Polecat branch. I started to worry. Dad and Reek sat on an old chestnut log, as cool as a cucumber.

Then I heard the train toot at the last house on Junaluska Creek. A little while later the noise grew so loud a person couldn't hear them self think. I had seen the train down in the valley around the switchyard; even stood and watched, them move cars around. The passenger train coming and going didn't raise an eye lid. This is a whole new sound. The mountains shook and my head throbbed with every lick of the piston. There is no sound like a logging train as it climbs up a steep mountain grade.

"Shaw. Shaw." Reek pointed toward the big column of black smoke snaking its way up the deep gorge. "She's a blowing and a goin."

To judge by the sound of the giant engine, it was traveling very fast. A little while later I felt the rails start to shake, even though the train had not come into sight. Each cough of the engine sounded like a bomb.

"Shaw. She's a comin now," Reek allowed as the black nose of the engine came around the point of the ridge, traveling about as fast as a body can walk. The trainman's head stuck out the small window on the side; his face covered with smut under his railroad cap.

The trestle shook and swayed as the engine crossed. I knew the thing was going to fall into the creek. I jumped down off the cross ties, really scared by now. The train didn't slow down as it reached us. The train man reached down, took my free hand, and lifted me into the cab. I let loose of my haversack as I swung in the air, but he just grinned and caught it in his other arm. Then he reached behind him for a greasy red bandanna. "Let me fix this on you," he shouted, as he wrapped it around my neck. "Keep the sparks from a going down your collar."

He wiped the smut off his face on the back of his striped railroad cap. The small cabin was full of cinders and ashes. Coal dust covered everything. Coal smoke, like burning sulfur, filled our lungs and burned our eyes. That and the heat from the boiler, forced us to stand in the doorway to catch our breath. Then we dodged tree limbs and laurel bushes as they raked along the engine. "Slide your feet, when you move about," he said, "or else you might step on a hot coal."

"Whew," I said.

"Ol number seven, she be a Shay engine," the engineer shouted in my direction. "Sidewinder type.

194

Made for pullin, not for speed. Pull the handle out of a white-oak maul, she will, but she travels slower than good news."

Dad and Reek swung aboard the coal car. They sat on the shiny coal, talking, well back of the cabin heat. Not me; I would stay up front from now to Christmas if they let me.

"She's thirsty," the engineer said, pulling a big brass lever down toward the floor of the cabin. The loud CHUG--Chug--chug of the piston slowed as we stopped at Ashturn Creek. A cool creek breeze filled the cabin at once. All at once, the whole train hissed. Snow white steam came from everywhere all at once--from down around wheels, from a pipe on top of the engine, even from the cabin. "Is it about to blow up." I said.

"Don't be a feared," the engineer's voice said from somewhere in the cloud, "She's just a catching her breath."

When the steam cleared, I saw Dad and Reek climb over some big boulders. There was no big water tower here, like in town. They pitched a poplar bark trough down to the engineer, who climbed out on the engine to its water box.

Steam again covered the mountain side as cold creek water hit hot steel. It popped and cracked and fried, like hot grease on a stove.

"Hold steady in the boat." The engineer put his hand on my shoulder as he climbed back in the cabin. "That creek water will calm down them pop-off valves."

Dad and Reek climbed back down into the cab. Both of them were wringing wet.

"Shaw. Shaw. That splash-dam needs a little shorin up."

"You drive while we work on the fire," the engineer lifted me onto the stool by the window.

"Shoot, I. . .I. . .I don't know how to drive this thing."

"Sure you do." He pushed the big brass lever up toward the top of the cabin. "This here's the throttle. Let her start slow, so she won't spin and break traction."

I looked out the little window as the train started to move in short lunges. I hardly felt them at first, but then they got stronger and longer. I strained hard, trying to see what lay ahead, but when the train turned to the left I saw only ten feet of track ahead. Making a right turn, the engine blocked the view of the rails, and I had to keep dodging the laurel limbs that raked the side of the train. Dad and Reek shoveled coal into the fire box while the engineer poked with a big iron rod. Flames shot back out into the cabin. Their clothes dried might near as fast as they had got wet.

Once the fire seemed to be to their liking, they went back to the coal car. I looked around a little while later and saw Dad, Reek and the engineer;

they were down on their knees, rolling dice against a big lump of coal. I didn't know Dad knew how to play dice, but I did know enough to keep my mouth shut to Mama.

We rounded a bend, and a Russian sow stood on the bank not five feet from my face. It was too late for me to be scared. She shook her head in my face. Too late to yell

"That old sow about to get you?" the engineer yelled over my shoulder.

"Yes sir! You sure right about that."

"She's here about ever trip." He pointed up in the hollow above her. "See all them pigs? I've counted over a dozen, several times. Look like ground squirrels with curly tails."

"Suey! SUEY!" Dad yelled as he threw two ears of yellow corn and a lump of coal up on the bank.

The sow gobbled up the corn while the little black spotted creatures scampered all around her, fighting for a taste. No wonder he saw her almost every trip.

At times, we were so close to the rock ledges I jerked my head back into the cabin. I figured the train would hit the rocks, for sure, but we passed with three or four inches to spare.

By mid-evening we crossed over the high tops. I saw the vast valley of the Nantahala River below. At once we started down a very steep grade. The engineer stood very close to me. Dad and Reek scurried over the back of the coal car, and ran back across the other cars, spinning the brake wheels as they came to them.

"Hold back there, girl." The engineer pulled the throttle down and pulled the brake lever back.

I heard the brake pads rub against the wheels. Each one seemed to have its own sound--one a high whine, another a deep growl. The engineer moved the throttle ever so little.

"He plays that engine like a fine fiddle," Dad said, as they climbed back in the cab.

"Shaw. Shaw, I'd say he do." Reek held the cabin wall to keep from falling forward.

"Cain't let the ole girl break traction," the engineer said. "She'll commence to slide. If a train don't break traction it'll never spin, slide--or or--or--wreck."

I shuttered every time the wheels slid a little or the sound of the brake pads changed pitch. The engineer touched my arm and yelled in my ear. "Lay steady in the boat! You'll get used to the noises. We ain't about to break traction. Nothing bad can happen to a train if we don't break traction."

Fifteen minutes later we were going along the Nantahala River in a slow climb. The cool river breeze made the inside of the cab just right. In some places the cribbing was so close to the river the train seemed to run on air, above the rushing water. The dice game started back up.

Once we left the river and started up the Buck Creek prong, the railroad bed ran in the creek. The train bounced and jerked to the point that I held on with all my might. At times the cow catcher in front pushed up water. Once the cars all leaned so far to the left, I felt sure we were going to flip.

"No way to bed the ties with dirt in the creek," the engineer said. "Don't worry none--were less than a half mile from camp."

The campsite was no more than seven rail cars on a siding under some big hemlock trees. They were small slab-covered boxes on wheels. None had windows or markings of any kind to set them apart; only the last one, on the far end, had smoke coming out of a rusty stove pipe run out the front end.

On the other side of the track a pole fence held several oxen and horses. They milled around and nibbled on hay scattered on the rocks.

"Let me bank this fire good," the engineer pitched the shovel into the coal. "Need to clean out these clinkers. I'll be on directly."

Trying to walk along the tracks, I almost fell. My body still swayed like the train had done all day. Dad and Reek laughed at me, but they were not doing much better.

"You don't talk while you're in the cook car," Dad said. "If a body growls about the food, they make him the cook till somebody else gripes."

"Shaw. Once Ol Sid---I cain't call his other name--said to the cook, 'Them thar's the saltiest beans I ever et.' Then he caught himself and says, 'But by thunder, that's the way I like'um.'"

By now, I could walk almost straight. Dad and Reek led the way to the car with the smoking pipe. Behind it was a lean-to with a dozen or more tables.

"Shaw. Shaw. That Ol Joe Hooker is one mean bastard. Never a kind word for any soul."

"Who's Joe Hooker," I said.

"He's the cook," Dad said. "He'll be your boss."

The man who met us at the door to the cook car had on the dirtiest apron I ever saw, around a fifty-inch belly. He shuffled around and poured coffee for the men before they sat down.

"Watch that thar tin cup--you ain't keer-ful," he said, "hit'll burn your mouth."

"This here's Little Quill," Dad said, rubbing my shoulder.

"Just call me Joe Hooker," the man said.

Moving like his shirttail was on fire, the cook soon had the table covered with food: beans, potatoes, bread, and hog stew.

The men started eating with their knives. I had seen Grandpa eat with a knife once, a while back, when we were at his house. For sure Mama would not put up with this at home. She got all out of sorts if Dad forked the butter. I looked around quick and saw there was not a fork or spoon in sight. Dad and Reek weren't having a bit of trouble. If I didn't learn to eat with my knife, I'd get powerful hungry in two weeks.

"Shaw, slide me that white sop," Reek said.

I stared at him. He stared back. I knew he wanted me to do something, but I didn't have no notion what.

"Slide me that whit. . . ."

Dad saved me when he passed the bowl of white gravy to Reek. Looks like I'll have to learn the talk as well as how to eat.

After a bit, I got some potatoes and bread down with my knife, but the beans kept rolling off. And I was afraid to even try the stew.

Pigs squealed as we raked the scraps into big lard buckets. The noise must have woke up the men up in the caboose. Eight loggers staggered up the tracks, some almost on their knees. Three still had empty pint bottles in their hands.

After we ate Dad led the way to the last car. Inside, bunks made out of ivy limbs sat along the side wall. Some had dirty mattresses, but most just had a pile of laurel leaves or pine needles for soft.

The little car was so narrow a body had to turn sideways to walk between the bunks. The smell of sweat and liniment was everywhere.

"Take this bed." Dad pointed to the cleanest bunk.

"Shaw, shaw." Reek flung his haversack on another bunk. "Think I'll go down and curry the stock."

"I'll hit them new saws a lick with a file," Dad said.

"Well, I'm a goin to sleep a spell." The engineer flopped down on a bunk. "Come midnight, I'll need to tend the fire if there's go'na be a head of steam come mornin."

I went with Dad. He placed the new cross-cut saw in a rack, then placed the little tool he called a spider against every tooth. He filed it with all the care in the world.

"Now I come to the tricky part," he said. "Puttin set in the teeth."

He placed a hand anvil against the tooth and tapped it with a small hammer ever so light. It sounded like a clinging of a sheep bell, off on a hillside. Only then would he look down the row of teeth. If one failed to suit him, he started all over again.

A drunken sawyer staggered by. "Git them misery whips good and sharp."

"It's a poor workman talks down about his tools like that," Dad said, holding up a nine-foot saw.

"Guess I'll go down and help Joe Hooker," I said. I knew Dad was a master saw filer, but the fine work with all the little hammers, files, spider, and anvil got on my nerves something fierce.

"All right." Dad never looked up.

Leaving now, I will miss the lecture the sawyer has coming. Besides, I wanted to be near the engine that sat still now and made a hissing sound as it let off steam.

I toted water and helped clean the cook car. After about an hour, I was sure the place was cleaner than ever before. Joe Hooker ran the cook car like he owned it; kept order and made sure his rules got followed. After the drunk loggers left he was all together different; joked and worked without saying a harsh word.

Joe Hooker pulled off his apron. "Go down to the third car. Old Abe Loudermilk, he whittles a pile of shavings ever night; fetch them so we can start us a fire come mornin. Be here ready to work at three."

After that I went to the creek to wash up. Even in the hottest part of the summer, the water raised chill-bumps all over me.

The camp was quiet long before dark. Save for the soft hissing sound of the engine. I slept good.

By the time I got to the cook car next morning, black smoke rolled from the train engine. That and the smell of wood smoke from Joe Hooker's fire hung heavy in the hemlock trees.

I had to run to keep everybody's bowl filled with potatoes, biscuits, fatback, gravy, and hen eggs. They downed coffee like spring water. Flapjacks and sorghum syrup set off the meal. The Timber Boss sat in the far corner sipping coffee, without any feelings showing on his face. By now, I was really hungry.

By 5:00 A.M. the men had left for the woods. Joe came out with a wooden spoon and handed it to me. We ate our breakfast without talking. I looked over in the corner and the timber boss had left.

"Go pour some coal oil on the men's beds," Joe said as we dried the last pots. "We've got to run them chinch-bugs out of them sleepin cars. I'll see you back here at ten."

I poured the oil on the beds, and in every crack in the bunk cars. I walked up the tracks toward the sound of screeching cables and winches filled the air. I wanted to see how the big logs were being loaded on the little cars.

The ground-hog skidder belched steam and rocked back and forth. Inch-thick steel cables anchored to big yellow locust trees kept it from turning over; still, it bounced a foot or better off the rails. The deafening scream of the winch cable hurt my ears as it pulled logs bigger than a truck tire, out of the canyon a quarter-mile away.

Reek walked along the top of a half-loaded rail car. He threw a set of shiny steel tongs down into the pile of logs. As they reached a certain log, he jerked the cable like you do a fishing line. The tongs set.

With his right hand over his head and first finger raised, Reek spun his wrist. I knew choker hookers and winch operators called this the "Highball sign." Another log came out of the pile and swung like a set of scales. He placed it on the car with one hand. For an hour or more, I watched and Reek only missed twice.

"That a pretty load of logs," the loader operator said, as we stood on the rails and waited for another car to roll into place. "Reek's the best that there's ever been, a thowin tongs and a stackin logs."

"Shaw. Nothin to it. Just bed the logs so they won't shift."

"If they shift airy bit," the loader man said, "it could cause the train to wreck."

That evening having some free time, I went back into the woods to watch the loggers work. I heard the clang of chains and the sound of a running horse coming down the steep skid trail, long before I saw anything. A mite scared, I climbed up on a narrow ridge, away from the skid trail. I watched them log.

"Jay!" a teamster yelled as the logs came close to the horse's feet. The mare ran into a cut-out on the high side of the trail. The ring slipped off the grab hooks as the logs passed. I heard the logs crashing on down the mountain, like they were no bigger than pencils, sliding off a stack of paper.

The teamster patted his horse on the head and told her. "Them logs were a nippin at your heels."

I felt the pride he had in his horse as he hung the trace chains on its gears, and the horse headed back up the trail.

"This sure is a bad place for horses to work." I said to myself, walking away.

I found Dad at the top of a bluff, driving the grabs into the logs with his usual care. "See here, the angle has to be just right for the ring to slip off when the horses jay," he said. "Yet set so they won't slip off when the horses are pulling."

A fellow wiped the sweat from his face with a bright blue bandanna. "This is rougher than a peach seed. Hit don't get no harder than this."

"Sure it does," Dad said. "You new hands will learn. Take that hollow up there: it's full of fine hemlock timber, only thing is it's too steep and rough for anything but oxen. The laurels so thick a body cain't run to get out of the way."

I pointed to the laurel thicket, that stretched for at least a mile. "How do you log through that?"

"Steers will ride down everything as big as a man's leg," Dad said.

"I want to go down there and watch," I said.

"Not while the overhead skidder are running."

I stood and watched the giant hemlocks fall up toward the head of the hollow. Some were so tall and had enough top limbs, they caused a breeze that shook everything within two hundred feet. The air was filled with the faint sound of axes. The crash of the timber breaking down, as the oxen logged, echoed out of the hollow.

The next day I walked, half a mile, to where they were logging on the north side of a ridge. The man chopping lead held an ax by its handle. The blade swung like a plumb bob. "I've got to figure which way the chestnut will fall." He cut a deep notch with an ax. When he stopped to catch his breath, he leaned on the ax handle. "If it ain't cut deep enough the tree split when it falls. Won't be fit for lumber."

Two men walked up and started pulling the long crosscut saw, across the base of the tree. I knew they would rather die than admit that anyone pulled a saw longer or faster than they did. Sweat poured as they climbed and worked like their boots were full hot coals.

"Their pay comes from thousands of feet of timber felled, in place of by the hour." Dad said that night, when I talked about how hard and fast they worked. "And they don't want to be outdone."

There was no time for anything but work. When the loggers came out of the woods at dark, they curried and fed the stock. Only then would they come to the cook car. After supper they worked on the tools and doctored and rubbed what ever hurt the most. There was fresh blood on their clothes most every night.

On Tuesday, the second week, they carried a young logger into camp with a gaping slash in his calf muscle that cut it might near in half. Blood spilled over the top of his already full boot. He bit his lip as they lay him on a table in the cook car. There was no way he was a day over eighteen.

"I was a bumpin knots and the ax glanced," he told Joe Hooker.

"It happens, son," Joe Hooker said.

"Will I be able to walk?" His voice trembled. "I got kids to feed! I got fields to tend! I need to work."

"It looks real bad to you," Joe Hooker said. "And it'll hurt like hell. But you won't be no cripple."

Joe put a spool of thread in some boiling water. He burned a needle with a match, all the while humming a little tune. "Coon up persimmon tree. Possum on the ground. Possum holler up. Shake them simmons down."

It bothered me that he seemed to be enjoying himself. And he couldn't carry a tune in a jug. On top of which he got the words mixed up half the time.

Then he stopped humming and turned to me. "Hold the lantern; just above his leg."

The two loggers that had carried the boy out of the woods, held the leg still while Joe cleaned it with the turpentine and camphor. Blood covered the table: it dripped on the floor. As Joe started sewing the muscle, down deep in the wound, I saw the sweat pouring off the young logger's face, like water over a rock. Joe hummed, "Bear he a sittin on gum stump. Possum come around--God damn this sorry son-of-a-bitching-thread." Twice more the thread broke and sent Joe into a rage. Both times he cussed the needle and thread for all they were worth. Then he started with that silly humming again.

Joe looked in the boy's face. "Cry, boy, if you have to; holler if it helps."

I'm not sure if Joe was trying to get him to cry. He went right on with the dumb tune. "Bear up a gum tree possum on a simmon stump." He had the words all out of order. My chest heaved but I held back the tears.

Joe worked, hummed, cursed, and worked for the better part of an hour. At last the wound came together. It looked better than I had hoped.

"Go fetch me some dry pine resin," Joe said, to me, as he jerked the last knot tight.

I was powerful glad to get out of the cook car. By the time I got back, the young logger lay fast asleep. Joe put the dry resin on the wound, and that stopped the bleeding around the stitches.

Three days later the logger was back working in the woods. He thanked Joe Hooker every day when he came for his meals.

"You will be going out soon," Dad said. "School starts in less than two weeks."

I knew there was no point in arguing with him, because Mama had one rule about school. She made it real plain. "If you live under my roof, you go to school and you learn."

They paid us off every Friday evening, even though some of us were not going anywhere to spend it. Most of the men sent their pay out to their womenfolk, by the train. This was my first real pay money. It felt good in my pocket.

"Let me make a run with the train tomorrow?" I asked the following evening. "My work is all caught up and I've got to get to the commissary and buy them boots."

"Joe needs you here," Dad said.

"I done and asked Joe. He can make do without me until we get back, early in he evening."

Dad got to his feet. "Guess you done and talked to the engineer, too."

"Shaw," Reek said, "let the boy go. The train man, he likes the boy; he'll watch atter him."

"All right," Dad said. "Behave, your Mama'll skin me alive if you get hurt."

It was hard getting any rest at all that night. I wiggled my toes; I could almost feel them A. A. Cutter boots on my feet now--tommorow. I'd rub them down with a beef bone, just like Joe Hooker had told me.

I woke up just before midnight. The engineer was already in the cab; the two brakemen were oiling the wheels. A cold drizzle made the old engine look new.

"Cold weather sets in early this far back," one brakeman said, as I passed.

"Hope this stuff don't freeze on the rails," the other allowed.

"Got some money?" the engineer, said, as he helped me climb into the cabin. "It's burning a hole in your pocket. Now you cain't wait to get to town, I reckon."

"I got to get them boots today," I said.

"Well, then, climb out there on the engine and bring me a handful of sand from the hopper."

Crawling with my fist closed was like trying to hold a fist full of oil. I spilled most of the hot dry sand, before I swung through the door.

"See any steam coming out of the hopper?" he asked.

"No, sir." I handed him what little sand I got there with.

The firebox glowed cherry red, like a black-smith's forge.

"Let's eat us a bite," the engineer said. "We'll leave in thirty minutes."

Joe Hooker had left some food on the stove. We ate without talking. "We've got to have plenty of fire," the engineer said when we got up to leave. "Got us the biggest load ever."

"Ready?" a brakeman asked, as we climbed onto the train.

"Let the brakes off, boys," the engineer said. "Start about half-way back."

I saw the cars backed up the creek; felt the weight of the logs as they pushed against the engine. Every time they freed up more brakes, the engine slid. I was a little scared. We had done gone and broke traction and we hadn't even got started. And this part of the track was not near as steep as some of the places ahead of us.

The engineer pulled back on the brake lever with all his might. He wiped and tapped every dial and twisted or pulled every knob he could find. The brakemen ran along the top of the log cars freeing up more brakes. The train lunged a little every time from all the weight. It jarred my bones like I'd been hit with a sledge hammer.

The rails sunk into the ground once we got off the creek bed. We came to a place where water ran along the side of the track; the train tilted to the left, I jumped toward the door. Wham! It settled back and threw me across the cab. I looked at the engineer, if he had seen me, he paid it no mind.

My heart skipped a beat every time we crossed a trestle. He never let the train gain any speed. The two brakemen ran along the logs, setting a brake here, letting one off there. Each brake squealed and screamed. Blue smoke and sparks flew as the brakes got hotter and hotter.

"Cain't break traction," the engineer said, time and time again.

We came to the steep hill everybody called Horse-Face Ridge. The brakemen ran along the cars, letting off the brake wheels for dear life. The train picked up more speed as we started to climb. Halfway up, it seemed the log cars would to push us clean to the top. Then all at once the weight shifted and we stopped. I leaned forward. It felt we were fixing to start sliding backwards.

"Cain't break traction." He slammed the throttle open.

The pop-off valves had been spewing great clouds of steam out near the wheels. Now it took everything the engine had to creep along. He pulled a wire, letting a small stream of sand fall in front of the drive wheels.

"This is a bad little stretch of track," he said. "No place to double out."

"What's doubling out?"

"On big mountains, if there's room, they build a siding. We pull half the load to the top and back it into the siding, then we go back and get the rest. Then we pick the first cars up and journey on. That way we don't have to keep shifting from pulling to braking so much. Here we still have to pull the first cars across. That's how you can break traction."

Once we crossed the top, we crept down the other side, no faster than a baby crawls.

"Being pushed up a steep grade and pulling hard going down another." I said, to myself. "It's no wonder it takes a long time to learn how to run a train.""

"It's a heavy load," one of the brakemen said as they climbed into the cab.

"Now comes the tricky part," the engineer said. Start settin the brakes. Use your own judgment."

"Judgment for what?" I said.

"Brake action," the brakeman said. "Too much and we'll stop; too little and we'll run away."

"Cain't break traction." I said.

The brakemen ran across the logs, tightening each brake wheel as they came to it. The brake pads gave a high-pitched squeal and from most of them, a trace of blue smoke shot out as they ground against steel.

"Too much speed," the engineer rested his foot on the boiler door lever. "We'll sling these top-heavy jimmy cars into the river, at Horse Shoe Bend."

He pulled back on the brake lever with both hands. "Throw more coal into the fire; we need to keep her old boiler red hot." Smoke and steam spouted out around the wheels, now. I threw coal into the boiler until flames shot out around the door.

I watched the brakemen way back up on the mountain. Sometimes curves hid the cars. At others, they seemed to be stacked up, on top of us, as they came down all the switch backs.

All at once, I heard a loud POP! We started to gain speed fast. I looked at the engineer's face. "What's. . . What? What's wrong?" I said.

"Somethin broke."

He pulled the brake lever with both hands. Now we moved at a fast clip. The engine rocked from side to side as the ground changed. This part of the track wasn't steep at all, but we took off, like we'd been shot out of a cannon. I looked back at the log cars stacked on the switch backs high above us. I couldn't tell how many were still up there, but it was a bunch.

I looked at the engineer. "Will we wreck?"

"Don't you worry none." He pulled on the wire cable that ran to the whistle. It gave out a sound; not like the toot-toot I had heard before. It sounded so loud and long; like the moan of a dying animal. Cold chills ran up my back.

"The engine ain't a holdin back like it ought to!" he said. "But we ain't broke traction yet."

He walked to the door and held up his hand the same way Reek gave the high sign to the skidder operator.

Seconds later I looked back and saw both of the brakemen jump off into a laurel thicket. The log cars rocked from side to side like something was trying to push them off the tracks. My belly had a knot in it hard as a fist.

"Will we wreck?" I said.

The ground only had a few steep places in it, but we kept building speed. At times we seemed to slow a little; at others we took off faster and faster.

"We may lose some of the cars once we reach Horse Shoe Bend," he said. "Else we'll be fine."

By now, we traveled so fast I couldn't make out the trees as we passed. On the other side, the river was just a mist below. The engineer held onto the seat, and watched back up the track, not saying a word.

I saw the steep bend up ahead; I knew what he had talked about. No way the train would go around it at this speed. In seconds, we were there.

Not knowing what had happened, or what to do about it, my mind sailed back to the last Sunday Dad and I were home. We stood along the north wall outside the meeting house. It poured the rain and we got back under the drip of the roof, while we waited for it to slack

Some womenfolks stood on the porch and talked of what they had heard went on in the logging camps.

"Why," A woman said, "I hear tell there's gambling, drinking, fighting and I don't know what-in-all goes on up there!"

"I wouldn't let no man of mine go near the place," another woman added.

The rain pounded down, as the women waited for their menfolks to bring the cars and buggies around. As always, we had walked to church. There was no way we could keep from overhearing every word. A woman from the low country, whose man held the job of lumber broker, joined in. "I hear tell they live like animals. They're just a bunch of low-down wood hicks."

Each in turn had something bad to say about life in the logging camps. I knew this didn't set well with Dad. He had spent the biggest part of his life in one.

We moved on down the side of the church, but couldn't get out of ear-shot, they were talking so loud. Dad turned his face to the wall.

"Why," The first woman said, "nothing but a bunch of heathens would go nigh one of them log camps."

Dad turned and walked right into the middle of the women. "More talk and gossip goes on here in fifteen minutes than in a month in the camp. I'll tell you ladies one thing about life in a log camp. It ain't exactly like living at the foot of the cross; then again, it ain't like living inside the gates of hell, neither!"

He pulled his old felt hat low over his eyes and lit out walking. I never felt the rain as I followed him home.

"Come here!" The engineer broke my spell.

He grabbed my left shoulder with his left hand and my right leg with the other. Before I could bat my eyes, he heaved me out the door.

"Wha. . . ."

I went through the air, my arms flailing like I was trying to swim. I hit the ground sprawled out on my belly. My mouth was full of sand and gravel. I had a hard time catching my breath.

The log cars passed me faster than I could count; they were just a blur. I knew any minute now one of them was going to turn over on top of me. Clawing at the gravel, I half-crawled, half-ran as fast as I could.

The cars rumbled and the brakes squealed. It hurt my ears. I felt like crying but was so scared, no sound came out.

Then another sound filled the air--logs, bumping and crashing into the river. "I hope the engine don't go too," I said, even though I knew nobody could hear.

BOOM! From around the bend I heard a sound that was even louder than all the thunder I had ever heard. The blast rocked the whole river valley. I ran across the small hump of sand and gravel that had built up in the bend. The cloud of steam, made it hard to see what had happened. I saw the engine, lying on its side in the water. Nothing moved inside.

I called out for the engineer, looked for him everywhere. I walked back along the track and looked for his footprints in the sand. Salty tears ran across my dirty lips.

I got hold of myself at the sight of horses running down the track toward me. The first two carried Joe Hooker and Dad.

"Are you all right?" Dad said.

"Ye--ah, but I cain't find the train man!"

"It was the explosion when the hot boiler hit the water that killed him," Dad said a few days after the funeral.

"Shaw," Reek said. "You're right about that. We even felt it in the deep cove where we were a workin."

"Some say they heard it over in Clay County," Dad said.

"Shaw, hit were the worst train wreck in these parts ever."

"Reckon why he didn't jump?" I said.

"He tried to ride it out, I figure." Dad said. "A body'll never know."

"What caused the wreck?" I said.

"Shaw. I don't recollect what caused it."

"They never said for sure," Dad said. "They searched that river bank for days—didn't find a thing."

It made Mama and Dad proud that I gave half my money when they took up for the engineer's family. I got the boots that following Christmas.

Time passes as it has a way of doing. One day I walked up the old railroad grade to do some trout fishing. I always stopped and looked off at the spot where the train wrecked. On up the river a ways, I walked and thought to myself. All at once my eyes

220

fixed on something shiny in the water. I climbed down the bank and picked up a big brass gear. The teeth were all badly worn. About four inches of them were broken off.   I wonder. . . .